Kent
Edited by Heather Killingray

 Young**Writers**

First published in Great Britain in 2005 by:
Young Writers
Remus House
Coltsfoot Drive
Peterborough
PE2 9JX
Telephone: 01733 890066
Website: www.youngwriters.co.uk

SB ISBN 1 84602 231 2

Foreword

Young Writers was established in 1991 and has been passionately devoted to the promotion of reading and writing in children and young adults ever since. The quest continues today. Young Writers remains as committed to the fostering of burgeoning poetic and literary talent as ever.

This year's Young Writers competition has proven as vibrant and dynamic as ever and we are delighted to present a showcase of the best poetry from across the UK. Each poem has been carefully selected from a wealth of *Playground Poets* entries before ultimately being published in this, our thirteenth primary school poetry series.

Once again, we have been supremely impressed by the overall high quality of the entries we have received. The imagination, energy and creativity which has gone into each young writer's entry made choosing the best poems a challenging and often difficult but ultimately hugely rewarding task - the general high standard of the work submitted amply vindicating this opportunity to bring their poetry to a larger appreciative audience.

We sincerely hope you are pleased with our final selection and that you will enjoy *Playground Poets Kent* for many years to come.

Contents

Cuxton Junior School

Yasmin Ali (10)	58
Ellie Webber (10)	58
Joshua Linares Stanley (10)	58
Cameron Fryer (10)	59
Ellen Le Brunn & Kate Brown (11)	59
Emily Martin (10)	59
Samantha Mussellwhite (11)	60
Jessica Chatfield (11)	60
Olivia Cobley (10)	61
Leila da Cunha Soares (11)	61
Olivia Guechtoum (10)	62
Oliver Watts (11)	62
Jack Harper (10)	63
Morgan Cooke (11)	63
Samantha Rankin (11)	64
Kitty Porter (9)	64
Sally Burrows (11)	65
Lauren Speirs (11)	65
Billie Watkins (10)	66

Elham CE Primary School

Josh Marden (9)	66
Bobby Andrews (8)	67
James Brookes (9)	67
Jake Theoff (9)	68
Sam Roud (9)	68
Darwin Hamilton-Radford (10)	69
Sophie Peers (8)	69
Bradley Andrews (8)	70
Sophie Bennett (9)	70
James Hirst-Beecham (9)	71
Tim Astbury (8)	71
Joshua Blackford (9)	72
Rebecca Allen (9)	72
Alice Olsson (8)	73
Connor Loome (9)	73
Fraser Nurse (9)	74
Abby Moffatt	74

Haddon Dene School

Ellie Wyatt (8)	75
Charlotte Stirling (9)	75
Jerome Edridge (9)	76
Matthew Speed (9)	77
Phoebe Sola (9)	77
Rowan De Bues (10)	78
Bronwyn Yeoman (9)	78
Bethany Johnson (9)	79
Rebecca Johns (9)	79
Millie Harris (8)	80
Mollie Ramos (7)	80
Johanna Pearson-Farr (8)	81
Charlie Cawdron (9)	81
Thierry Preston (8)	82
Josh Yeoman (8)	82
Lugain Rfidah (8)	83
Harry Price (7)	83
Gabriella Panteli (8)	84
Grace Murray (7)	84
Jenny Dening (9)	85
Daniel Jackson (8)	85
Melissa Brill (8)	86
Kyri Papa-Adams (8)	86
Bradley Keens (10)	87
Bradley Jarman (8)	87
Emily Mitchell (8)	88
Giorgia Amato (10)	88
Connor Winter (9)	89
Poppy Lawson (9)	89
Pierre Laurens (9)	90
Charlie Mitchell (8)	90
Irzam Ahmed (11)	91
Ryan Coleman (8)	91
Molly Hirst (11)	92
Ashley Bourne (11)	92
Francesca Nadin (11)	93
Charlie Cragg (8)	93
Tessa Dening (11)	94
Jennifer Pearson-Farr (11)	95
Dylan Mitchard (11)	95

Ightham Primary School

Nicola Carter (9)	96
Chloe Penfold (7)	97
Karly Penfold (10)	98
Alice Watson (8)	99
Honey McElhill (11)	100
Chloe Jessop (9)	100
Courtney Whitehead (8)	101
Gabrielle Harvey (7)	101
Imogen Harvey (9)	102
Francesca Bennell (9)	102
Callie Birch (9)	103

Newington Junior Foundation School

Antony Clement (8)	103
Paige Wilson (9)	104
Allan Ladd (8)	105
Abbigail East	106
Jasmine Queen (9)	106
Stuart Sheppard	107
Amy Cook (9)	107
Kiah Harding	108
Marissa Clay (9)	108
Jack Breach (8)	109
Sinead Parker (8)	109
Emma Wicks (9)	110
Daniel Powell (8)	110
Jamie Goldfinch (8)	111
Luke Menzies (10)	111
Jack Dexter (8)	112
Daisy Richford (10)	113
Atlanta Amato (9)	113
Rhiannon Rose (11)	114
Ryan Maudlin (11)	114
Ryan Rodway (11)	115
Masuma Aktar (11)	115
Charmaine Wheeler (11)	116
Jacob Burton (11)	116
Thomas Newing (11)	117
Leanne Handy (11)	117
Katie Martin (10)	118

Nonington CE Primary School

Normandy Primary School

Sophie Wallis	139
Chloe Haynes (10)	140
Lucie Eyles (11)	140
Hannah Beacock-Evans (11)	140
Charlie Samuelson (11)	141
Ellie Kember-Hollands (11)	141
Sasha New (10)	142
Jay Johnson (11)	142

Parkway Primary School

Voke Oyeye (11)	143
Matthew Knight (11)	143
Victoria England (10)	144
Derrick Major (11)	144
Annie Jones (11)	145
Christine Tang (11)	146
Sarah Baker (11)	146
Amanda Pappoe (10)	147
Laura Keane (11)	147
Zahra Sadi (10)	148
Georgie Benton (10)	148
Shane Murphy (11)	149
William Jenkins (11)	149
Tosin Osiewu-Seriki (10)	150

Pembury Primary School

Dominic Woodcock (11)	150
Marcus McCloud (11)	151
Christopher Ithier (11)	151
James Davis (10)	152
Jack Welch (11)	152
Rachel Drapper (11)	153
Bethanie Walker (10)	153
Rosie Woodgate (11)	154
Oliver Collard (11)	154
Rebecca Brett (11)	155
Molly Clement (11)	155
Zoë Powell (11)	156
Ann-Marie Philpot (10)	156

The Poems

Laughter

Laughter is yellow
like a multicoloured
clown telling fantastic jokes.

Laughter sounds like
an echoed noise that
comes from people's mouths.

Laughter tastes like
a scent that comes
from your mouth.

Laughter smells like
a boy enjoying himself
with his best friends.

Laughter looks like
someone's face lighting
up with a glow.

Laughter feels like
your face
being stretched.

Laughter reminds me
of all the good times
I had with my grandad.

Joe O'Grady (11)

My Dad - Cinquain

My dad,
Takes me fishing,
On a sunny weekend
And I always have a great time
With him.

Emma Stiles (10)
All Saints CE School

Word Party

Spiteful words can make you cry
Happy words can make you fly
Rude words have a fight
Scary words go and hide
Caring words say, 'Hello'
Loving words hold crimson hearts
Silly words make people laugh
Swear words hurt my heart
Clumsy words give you a fright
Bouncy words keep on jumping
Peaceful words are so relaxing
Small words should stand on cardboard boxes
Shouting words are always late
Scary words make me want to shake
Sweet words hold my hand
Holy words are words that we pray
Historical words are late in the date
Complicated words we think are hard
Sad words fall into a puddle
Foreign words that you can't understand
Swear words you can't stand
So when the party is over
The moon comes out and we start over.

Charlotte Carré (9)
All Saints CE School

Lovely Colours

Blue is the sky with white boats sailing across it
Pink is a munchy, enjoyable piece of candyfloss I can't wait to eat!
Yellow is a rubber dinghy, floating in the sky
Green is on top of the trees in the rainforests with lots of insects
in them
Silver is the colours of stars when they sparkle
Purple is the colour of the lavender in my garden
Red is the colour of roses in my friend's garden
Black is the colour of the dark night sky
White is the colour of our new fantastic building
Gold is the colour of a shining sword
Brown is the colour of a worn out branch
And all of these colours are in the beautiful rainbow!

Rebecca Payne (10)
All Saints CE School

What Is The Moon?

The moon is a yellow football,
Being kicked high in the sky by David Beckham.
It is yellow candyfloss, being held in the dark.
It is a grey blob on black paper with holes in.
It is a yellow bowling ball being thrown down a black lane.
It is mouldy cheese with mice bites in.
It is a circle cut out of a banana put on a black carpet.
It is a yellow beanbag on a black sofa.
It is a circular desert in the night sky.

Elizabeth Early (10)
All Saints CE School

Firework Display Day

Bang go the fireworks
Hiss goes the Catherine wheel
Crackle go the sparklers
Ssshhh, it's too much noise.

Whizz goes the rocket
Roar goes the sky
Oh what a wonderful sight
Ssshhh, it's too much noise.

Squelch go the boots in the mud
As someone goes up the path
The firework, ooh *bang*
Ssshhh, it's too much noise.

The space goes *crash, boom, bash*
As it goes, we all look up
I love that firework
Ssshhh, it's too much noise.

The firework goes *whizz, boom, whizz, boom*
That was called the paper lion
The end of the fireworks
Can I have a sausage Mum?

No, it's too much noise!

Rebecca Bertolla (10)
All Saints CE School

Words

Caring words will make you jump
Careless words you might have a bump
Tough words are a bit too rough
Rude words, 'Now that's enough'
Sad words make you cry
Bouncy words you can jump to the sky
Scary words there in the night
Stupid words aren't that bright
Frightening words are very scary
Happy words just like Mary
Swear words make you stamp your feet!
Hungry words, 'Oh can I have some meat?'
Holy words, one story is about Noah
Small words they just get lower
Historical words are about time
Loving words, 'Oh, that man's mine'
Expensive words have a lot of money
Poor words just have a bare tummy
Sweet words give out roses
Snap!
The dictionary closes.

Philip John (10)
All Saints CE School

What Is The Sky?

The sky is a light blue piece of paper
With candyfloss dropped into spaces.
It is blue wallpaper
Dotted with shiny stars.
It is a blue carpet stuck on a wall
With a sun on it.
It is a blue tapestry
With cross-stitched stars embroidered on it.
It is a blue birthday card
With an orange, glowing sun on it.
It is a turquoise blanket
With silver bows on it.
It is a dark blue ocean
With a lump of cheese on it.
It is a lovely lake
With a wonderful canary-yellow duck on it.

Holly Pearce (10)
All Saints CE School

What Is . . . The Ocean?

The ocean is a blob of ever growing ink
It is a blue blanket that comes to life
It is a blue folder that is getting full
It is a dark quilt that has someone tossing around underneath
It is a puddle that never dries up
It is a piece of tissue paper with a cardboard fish jumping out of it
It is a child's eye that never changes colour
It is an extending carpet that never wears out
It is a school jumper that is always clean
It is a curtain that is always closed
It is a blue pair of jeans that are always moving
It is a blue raincoat that is always wet
It is a book that has never been opened
It is a blue whiteboard pen that never stops writing
It is a jewel glistening forever and ever.

Claire Croucher (10)
All Saints CE School

Swap Ya

I'll swap ya a . . .
Rubber duck
A tiny truck
A leather bag
A French flag
A red ruby
All for a cool Skoobie!

Nooo!

I'll swap ya a . . .
£500
An odd sock
A golden lock
A cup of coffee
With a bar of toffee
A tin of glue
For a holiday in Peru!

Nooo!

I'll swap ya a . . .
Red ruby
200 Skoobies
A pencil case
A rubber face
All for your hiding place!

Maybe *yes!*

Alice Wheeler   (10)
All Saints CE School

Expressions!

Hi kids, my brain's full
Stay to listen to my words . . .

Violent words always kill
Telling words always have a chill
Strong words give a fright
Park words fly their kite
Coloured words change colour
Dark words get duller and duller
Small words are very light
Fighting words have so much might
Stupid words live in a lump
Clumsy words have a bump
Loving words get married
Baby words live in a carriage
Money words have to pay
Jumping words jump all day
Careless words always fall
Mighty words can break a wall
Boring words have nothing to do
Rude words look like a fool
Alphabetical words recite the alphabet
Gambling words always bet
Mouthy words always talk
Leggy words always walk
Villain words are really bad
Crazy words are extremely mad
Joker words are so funny
Egg words are produced from an Easter bunny

Sorry kids my brain's burst
Now it's hollow, I've told it all to you.

Gurinderbir S Padam (10)
All Saints CE School

Night-Time Nightmare

A dark sky
A cold night
An old house with a dimming light
Walk up to the house and open the door
Hear a creaking from the floor.

Take a step in and look around
Look up to the ceiling and down to the ground
The door shuts behind me and sticks tight
And in a sudden flash out goes the light.

A spooky cackling you can hear
As a bewitching eye begins to peer
It peers at me this way, it peers at me that way
When out from behind it pops, a pure black cat.

I try and get past it without being seen
But it appears that this eye is very mean.

A witch comes by me counting 1, 2, 3
And saying she is going to eat me
She ties me up to a chair
And her nostrils give a flair.

I see a potion on a shelf
So I try and untie myself
But before I can do anything
I hear a rather loud ping.

The witch had turned into stone
Then finally with a groan
I manage to untie myself
I get the potion off the shelf.

No more dark sky,
No more night
For now it is the morning bright.

Sophia Patricia Mai Patel (10)
All Saints CE School

Riddle # 1 - Which Magazine Do I Collect?

My first is in *three,* but not in *two,*
My second is in *don't* and also in *do,*
My third is in *tree,* but not in *plant,*
My fourth is in *carry* twice but never in *can't,*
My fifth is in *ivy,* but not in *rose,*
My sixth is in *eyeball,* but not in *nose,*
My seventh is in *Liverpool,* also in *Leeds,*
My eighth is in *flowers* and twice in *weeds.*

My ninth is in *sixty* as well as *ten more,*
My tenth is in *occupy,* but not in *bore,*
My eleventh's in *lollies,* but not in *toffee,*
My twelfth is in *tea* and also in *coffee,*
My thirteenth is in *Nicola,* but not in *Gary,*
My fourteenth is in *christen,* but not in *marry.*
My fifteenth is in *tell* and also in *direct.*

Which magazine do I collect?

Answer: Horrible Science.

Daniel Droscher (11)
All Saints CE School

A Cat

Claw grippers
Beautiful purrers
Awesome biters
Gymnastic jumpers
Excellent pouncers
Crime watchers
Ace mousers
Evil creatures
Meat eaters
Cunning cats.

Amy Cooley (11)
All Saints CE School

Riddles

Chair
In the classroom
A thing with no hair
But yet it has legs.

Any colour, they may be
Altogether an army of 30
With legs, 120.

You may squash me
But I won't break
As I can hold the heaviest weight.

Love
My first is in *clover,* but not in *sewer*
My second is in *orange* and in *mower*
My third is in *van,* but not in *door*
My last is in *egg,* but not in *raw.*

Alex Bates (11)
All Saints CE School

What Am I?

I float past making you stare in awe
I make shapes and dance until I get
Angry and turn grey, but I never understand
Why everybody runs away and goes indoors.
What am I?

Answer: A cloud.

Lucy Toms (11)
All Saints CE School

In The Playground

I was running in the playground
When I lost my ear, but it was found
They found it up the Hokey-Cokey tree
Which is taller than three of me.

I was jumping in the playground
When my knee got lost, but it was found
They found it in the teacher's coat
The one who's crazy and has a pet goat.

I was skipping in the playground
When my arm fell off, but it was found
They found it in the bathroom sink
Now it's mouldy, gone yucky pink.

I was sleeping in the playground
When my toe came off, but it was found
They found it in a smelly bin
Right inside a tuna fish tin.

I was singing in the playground
When all my teeth fell out, but they were found
They found them in Mrs Locket's shoe
It had a hole and some went through.

I was sneezing in the playground
When my nose shot off, but it was found
They found it in the kitchen cupboard
Guess who had to get it out . . . Mother Hubbard!

Rebecca Geraghty (11)
All Saints CE School

What Is . . . The Moon?

The moon is a blob of ink
On a black piece of paper
The moon is a soft snowball
Floating in the air
The moon is a white circle
On a blue piece of paper
The moon is a white blob of ink
Floating in the sky
The moon is a holey piece of cheese
Floating in mid-air
The moon is a white blob of paint
Splattered on the sea
The moon is a blob of white candyfloss
Resting on a river
The moon is a white stone
Flying in mid-air
The moon is a white pupil
With a blue background in your eye
The moon is a fluffy sheep
Flying in the sky
The moon is a white speaker
With a blue background on a CD player
The moon is a white tooth
Resting in a blue mouth.

Jacqueline Williams (11)
All Saints CE School

Wonderful World

I wondered through the countryside
I saw the birds that always glide
I was a soft, white floating cloud
There were no dogs barking loud.

I touched my hair which is soft as a kitten,
I looked down at my baby blue mitten
Then I found a white flower
As tall as a very tall shower.

The sun was like a lump of butter
I then saw a butterfly flutter
The world seemed quiet and calm
Just like my very still white palm.

The massive sky was light blue
The gentle breeze smelt like glue
The trees were as tall as a mountain
Then suddenly I thought of a fountain.

My world then turned upside-down
Like a horrible and mean clown
But then I had to think and find
If it was just my wild mind.

Louise Page (11)
All Saints CE School

Guess The Riddle Of The Pupils

Who are these rhinos the rampagers
Who came to your class with horns rampaging of course?

Who are these rhinos that always race,
Who never stop rolling,
Running to attack,
Always ready to attack
With hair and ugly skin?
Do tell the teacher.

John Cruickshank (10)
All Saints CE School

Stool

Why do you stand there
All silent and alone?
Why do you have legs
But never walk?

Why are you so cold
And never say a word?
Why are you so firm
Inside your box?

Why when we close your box
You never struggle out?
Why don't you breathe at all
Why don't you talk?

What are you
Who shows no emotion
What is your species friend?
Who are you?

Answer: Stool.

Amber Colyer (11)
All Saints CE School

When I Went To School Tomorrow

When I went to school tomorrow
I laid a flea
And lost my knee
And sailed to sea
With a wooden leg
So I had to flipping beg
Doing so I lost my key.

I went there to get home
I ended up in Rome
I wanted my mummy.

Mitchel Benham (10)
All Saints CE School

When I Went Bowling

When I went bowling with my friends,
We all went in the men's
I bowled a ball down the lane
But unfortunately it shot back at me again.

We started to grow hungry soon,
So we pressed the button to go to the moon
We landed soon and we were shocked at what we saw
As we had been expecting more.

We were surrounded by delicious cheese,
But suddenly saw a swarm of bees
'Let's grab some cheese and run away,'
I heard my friend Sam say.

We had done exactly what she said,
We carried some cheese and off she led
We went back to the bowling centre
And she gave me back the chips I lent her.

Angela Wright (11)
All Saints CE School

What Am I?

High in the sky
Like a black sack I lie
I'm filled with joy by the twinkling white around me
England travels on
While Australia comes round
On the other side I see a huge ball of fire
What am I?

Answer: The dark night sky.

Jonathan Lindsey (11)
All Saints CE School

Heather

Scowling
Like a mad cat
Growling like a lion
Crazy, lazy, hazy Heather
Crazy!

Crazy
Step cautiously
There is no way out of
Scowling, scary, hairy Heather
Oh no!

Oh no!
Run away she
Might get you and pull you
In, Heather's bone-crunching teeth
Run away.

Joseph Cubitt (11)
All Saints CE School

End Poverty

People helper
Food giver
Heart warmer
Sick killer
Shelter giver
Blood donator
Clothes giver
Life saver
Sadness killer
Happiness giver!

End poverty!

Michael Letchford (11)
All Saints CE School

Yellow!

A yellow sun in the sky so bright
Not around in the still of night
The daffodils swaying in the breeze
Alone I stand until I sneeze
The roses and tulips are all around
It's quiet here, there's not a sound.

Yellow is the colour of so many things
Just like a canary as it sings
The butter is hard and will not spread
Unlike mustard upon my bread
The yellow custard is lumpy and cold
It is my grandad wrinkly and old.

The balloon is thunder popping so loudly
I wear my yellow shoes so proudly
Balls, balls they go so far
Just like my dad in his new fast car
Lines on the road so bright and bold
They lie side by side so long, so cold
The sun goes down, here is night
The brightness gone - the sun says
Goodnight!

Laura Tullett (11)
All Saints CE School

Mirror

Why do you show the same?
Why do you copy me?
Why do you follow my every move?
Why do you look like me?
Are we identical twins?
Why do we wear the same?

Gemma Cole (11)
All Saints CE School

What Is Yellow?

Yellow is the sunset
It's bright and bouncy too
Brightens up the day
And gives us things to do
Yellow is a flower
The heat of your town
Bananas and a melon
A yellow spotted gown.

The sound of yellow is
Tweet! Tweet! Tweet!
The colour of your socks
Sitting on your feet
Yellow is always happy
You can find it anywhere
Yellow is always helpful
And always makes things fair.

Yellow is a warming colour
Whatever is the weather.

Yellow makes the sunshine
Yellow makes it warm
It also makes the sun go down
But still shines on at dawn.

Bethany Mitchell (11)
All Saints CE School

A Lonely Brick

A lonely brick
Crying for happiness as the clouds grow dark
Little by little his smooth face is worn away by tears
None can understand his sadness
He is surrounded by a large family
He is not alone, yet he is,
For he is a white island in a brown sea.

Joe Kellett (11)
Benenden CE Primary School

The Ageing School

My school is old
The bricks are worn away by wet weather
The steps have dents where feet have been
Running and thumping.
The walls have tattooed scars
The higgledy-piggledy roof grows green fluffy moss
Circular windows have shut their eyes to the blinding ray of the
golden sun, never to be opened.
The stained marks will not go away and strange things are written.
Fading on the soft sandstone of the porch.
Mottled bricks baked into the wall
All the same, but different as their ancient markings tell them apart
The walls age with each passing day
And become sander, more vulnerable
Where the bell once had a proud job of ringing, now has birds nesting
My school is old
But young.

Phillipa Illman (11)
Benenden CE Primary School

Old School

The dark, damp shelter pegs rusting in the rain
As the cruelly broken bricks just about remain
But the ragged 'S' shaped brasses crippled in vain.

Do not disturb the twiglet nests for there is no intelligence
And if you stand on the bendy steel it will have no existence.

The holey shelter wall is splintered by bullet's smoke
Thus the crimpled chimney takes no smoke
Just go on to see some broken bricks and cement

The school will love a lot longer
Though only if you have children to wander.

Thomas Aldous (11)
Benenden CE Primary School

The Prehistoric School

The pale colour of the front of the aged school
Is still there as if it hadn't been fingered
By the grubby hands of the yapping school children.

The frayed ropes of the cricket green perish
Away as they are ready to be replaced.

The ancient grooming birds still grumble to
Each other about all the things they have seen.

The wet playground lets the water of the sky
Seep through its layers of unforgettable grazes and bruises.

The mildewed bricks which have been there forever
Are forever and finally cracking.

The pencil engraved tables are scarred for life.

The vulnerable graffiti marks on the walls keep
Crying out for the pain of the building.

The delicate wooden frames of the ageing school
Porch roof creak as if they had come to
The end of their unimportant lives.

Lewis Gray (11)
Benenden CE Primary School

This School

New electronics bring down the walls
As our greed asks for more and more
Cracks scarred into the walls forever
By the live wire youth running galore!

Smothered bricks from downward generations,
As the thumping sphere battles onwards for its goal
A sad blanket surface stone cold still
Once used to be awash with blazing hot air.

This place is but a ruin
We have our green still shining in its young sheen
And the grand school, so old, yet young.

Josh Smith (11)
Benenden CE Primary School

As A School Fades To Darkness

Tattered and tramp-like body
Its skin strangely and anciently coloured
Red and brown and bruised in blotchy black
More bruises appear as its journey continues.

Exquisitely created window frames
Looking down upon us
Their magnificently engraved facial features
Holding and supporting their shiny glassy eyes.

The evil dark mind at the top of this body
Crowded with long past souls
Screaming voices
And scary memories of their homes.

An ancient bomb shelter
The arthritic right hand of the body
Holding and processing people of the past
To be misused in the present.

This body is crumbling and cracking
As a school fades to darkness.

James Bourne-Taylor (11)
Benenden CE Primary School

Old Crumbled Bricks

The whining broken bricks howl in the wind
The shelter, an essential part of the school in the war
Nobody really knows what it's for now
The 'S' shaped metal plates reinforce the crumbled walls
Sandstone, which is holding up the cold brick chimney
Crumbled man-made bricks
Did anyone look at them?
The bricks wear as the years go by
Graffiti on the decaying porch
Maybe this school will shine again.

Robbie James (11)
Benenden CE Primary School

The Dark School

The old primary school
With all the devil cracks.

Looking like three claws have
Scarred the brickwork for life.

The disturbing black rusty
'S's' have been stuck to the wall
For too many years.

The blackened out circle windows
Will they ever be opened again?

The repulsive soggy moss on
Top of the tiles, will it ever
Stop growing?

Harry Sullivan (10)
Benenden CE Primary School

The Dying Stones

Circular windows have closed
Their eyes to the cruel bitterness of time
Unable to face the changes
That lie before them
As the battered stone that protects them
Watches in horror at the change
Of the people they have protected
The walls are slowly dying
To be returned to the ground where
They will be forgotten by all they have watched
Where their knowledge will be forgotten forever.

Jake Parkin (10)
Benenden CE Primary School

A School Waiting For Demolition

The tower has stood for ages
Through wind and rain, through good and bad
It has seen more than any mortal
It longs for people to enter its welcoming bosom
But the ages have left their mark
The bricks are worn and marked and they
Yearn for the passion they have lost.

The circular faces that won't witness
The evaluation of the young
No more shall they bear the light which before lit their
Transparent complexion and shone with
Golden, heavenly glory.

The huge iron 'S' stays fast to the
Crumbling wall holding steady as the
Hundreds of ancient bricks crumble in chorus
Children running in an old cracked playground
A school waiting for demolition.

Sebastian Carnwath (11)
Benenden CE Primary School

Untitled

The cracked and cobwebby bell
Up in its tower no longer rings
Once it told children to come to school
Quickly running through the door,
Rushing to their classes,
Through the years the bricks have worn away
It is time to get a new school.

Bradley Milham (11)
Benenden CE Primary School

The Black School

Dark rusting 'S' shaped devil marks
Remain scarred on the disintegrating bricks
Shadowed in abstract human features.

Violently carved stone blocks
From eternities ago are graffitied
In ancient evil.

The scorched black surface
Of a primitive withered fireplace
Which holds many secrets and hears many lies.

The school may be old and wrinkling
But on the inside it is laughing and smiling
As its spirit is young and free.

Hugo Hensley (11)
Benenden CE Primary School

Farewell School

From dingy and dark to a smooth
Tarmac road travelling through all-knowing time.

Cramped bomb shelter employed in
The everlasting expansion of tension
When the screaming siren goes up.

Roof tiles slowly demolished by
The thousands of bird talons scraping
And clawing all around.

Scarred sandstone revealing many
Passers of the long years.

Rory Wheatley (11)
Benenden CE Primary School

The Ageing Bricks

The scattered bricks are old and worn
And cracking as they grow ancient
They gaze happily at the children
Laughing in the playground.

Dates from long ago are engraved in
The soft sandstone of the old school
Above the birds nest in the ageing roof
Talking to the children at any opportunity.

The black and white panels stand proud
Around the roof of the old school building
Staring at passers by and calling out
Names of those who once stood there.

Lucy Mumbray (11)
Benenden CE Primary School

What Am I?

My companions are scattered and unevenly sized
RH Chambers, a voice of the past, stained on my ancient sandstone
I am battered and rotting
Scratchy white paint falls from the window sill above me
I am earth coloured and even come in rust
My friends and enemies are all antique
Cracks are formed in us because of old age
Blue ink is smudged on our surfaces
I cannot see, but I can hear
Will I ever open my eyes again?

I am a brick.

Jessie Barker (11)
Benenden CE Primary School

The Messages

The old engravings declare their loved ones;
They cry out and tell me that their eyes are closed forever.

The widowed windows sit there, their sunlight has been stolen;
A small amount of happiness has been left in the soul.

The crying of the sky, makes teardrops fall,
To the old wreckage of a playground.

Through the years, the messages will fade away
In the aged stones of the porch.

These messages tell me that our school
Is fading.

Beth Massey (11)
Benenden CE Primary School

The Living School

The school building is alive within its depth
The rugged bricks communicate children's hysterical laughter
Concentric discs lighten the wall of blocks creating an eternal ring
Vibrant tyres delight the infant ideas of play
Ivy caves over the aged posted obstacle
Wounds in the stone mark the date of our school
Birds sing in the sky-scraping trees
While the school stands young yet old
The building has stood for many generations
And its use must now come to an end.

Lauren Walter (11)
Benenden CE Primary School

Circle Window

Circle window saw victorious play
Men came and shut its eyes for eternity
All it hears are children laughing
Who are they?
Are they my friends that saw my new shining glass when I
Was born and my beautiful carvings?
Who knows?
Will my eyes ever open again?

Charlotte Greenhill (11)
Benenden CE Primary School

Unnoticed

The grubby roof tiles with mossy hedgehogs on
Lay uneven and chipped watching over the
School children from the rotting structure of the roof.
Ancient carving tattoo the sandstone walls of the outer porch
The charcoal black flap for cleaning the chimney
Lies silent on the playground wall watching everyone
Who goes past although it is never noticed.

Nicholas Heath (10)
Benenden CE Primary School

The Classroom Door

The dented door has creaking hinges
And ancient fingerprints of children who have left their mark
Not for much longer
Time has moved on.

Luke Bennett (11)
Benenden CE Primary School

When The World Was Young

When the world was young and the land was bare
Nature and wildlife were not yet there
No one knows how it started really,
Although many people have a theory;
A ferocious fireball came down our way
But torrential rain washed it away
There, rivers were formed and fish soon appeared.
And other animals cautiously neared
Then monkeys changed to man and man changed the world
As well as women too, intelligent, hair straight, crimped or curled
They all hatched plans to make the world better
Developed literature, language and letter.
Now we have electricity and new sources of light
Boxes with characters in, all ready for a fight.
Our world keeps on changing and will never be the same,
From global issues to different types of game.
And I wonder something that I'll never know
What will the world be like in a hundred years or so?
So when I pick up a pen, I don't stand there grinning
I think to myself, this wasn't here at the beginning!
It definitely wasn't here when they world was young.

Matilda Slight (11)
Chiddingstone CE Primary School

My Week

Monday is the day for playing cricket
Tuesday is the day I tell Dad about my wicket
Wednesday is the day I give my hair a trim
Thursday is the day I go for a swim
Friday is the day I wish I could grow tall
Saturday is the day I play football
Sunday is the day my room gets smelly
Because my friends and I watch football on the telly.

Jack Day (10)
Chiddingstone CE Primary School

Norman

You sit there all innocent
What a funny pose
You've been digging
I can tell from your dirty nose.

You bark at hot air balloons
As they float past in the sky
Mum calls you a midget
Because you're only twenty-two inches high.

You are a top dog
You've been to Crufts the dog show
I love you Norman
You're my favourite you know.

Love and attention
Is all you seem to need
Norman you soppy dog
You're from a scary breed.

He's not your average Rottweiler
As I'm sure you can see
I wish he were even smaller
So he could sit on my knee.

Hazel Banham (11)
Chiddingstone CE Primary School

I Can See The Cross

I can see the cross
The cross can see me
God bless the cross
God bless me.

I can feel the cross
The cross can feel me
God bless the cross
God bless me.

Tom Critchley (10)
Chiddingstone CE Primary School

Noises

I wake up to the bright new day
To turn on the radio and hear Jonathan Ross say:
'Hello and good morning'.

I get up and go into the kitchen
The TV is killing me
As my headache gets worse.

The world is full of noises
Big and small
Our ears are finding it hard
To listen to it all!

We live in these noises that smother the earth
Listening to them from birth
Sweet birds singing
And comforting sounds
Give us life and make us proud.

We live in these noises that smother the Earth . . .

Margot Goldman-Edwards (9)
Chiddingstone CE Primary School

Sports

Some sports are tiring
Some are quite easy
Some sports may be boring
Some sports are extremely fun
Some sports are to represent a place
Although my sport is better than the rest
Football is easy, football is tiring, football is not boring
and football is fun.

Josh Cole (9)
Chiddingstone CE Primary School

My Only Friend

I have a friend
I don't know his name
Sometimes we like to run around;
Sometimes we play a game.

We are aliens in disguise
When we play this game
Travelling around the solar system;
From Jupiter we came.

My friend is really good
At playing our game called 'Space'
He could actually be the alien;
Not far from the human race.

One day I saw him crying
And he said he had to go
Back to his home in outer space;
He thought I ought to know . . .

That he is an alien from miles away
Just like the one in our game
It makes me feel bad that he has to go;
Like I'm the one to blame.

I never saw him again after that
He only used to live round the bend
He was always there when I needed him most
My only friend
My only alien friend.

Georgina Kleinschmidt (10)
Chiddingstone CE Primary School

Cub Camp

Fun and games
Activities galore
Time for bed
Hope my friends don't snore.

Larking around
Having chocolate cake
Spooky stories
Staying up late.

Freezing cold
All the night
Cannot move
Sleeping bag zipped up tight.

It was fantastic
Went like a dream
What I enjoyed most was
Absolutely *everything!*

Joshua Heaps (9)
Chiddingstone CE Primary School

Summer

What lovely red roses
I will put them into pretty posies;
I saw a horse and it was the colour of golden syrup
There I saw a loose stirrup.

Roses, roses, roses.

There are lovely fish;
Some of them are black as liquorice;
The sun is out everywhere;
Look it's over there.

Danielle Hunt (11)
Chiddingstone CE Primary School

Arsenal - The Cup Final

The ref has blown his whistle, the big game is underway
Both teams are out there to show who can play
Under the great pressure of Cup Final day.

The atmosphere is growing
There are chances either way
Who will get the needed goal,
Before the half-time break, on Cup Final day.

Half-time has arrived, the tension hard to take
No side just quite yet, have caught the other on the break
This one is far from over, the second half yet to come
Who will emerge from this one, as the happy victorious ones?
On Cup Final day.

The second half is looming, the score is still 0-0
The teams are ready on the pitch, to kick off once again
On Cup Final day.

The chanting is getting even louder, to spur their team to the end
20 minutes left now, one last drop of effort
On Cup Final day.

Could this be the last attack the Arsenal get?
We are deep into added time with no one yet ahead
The crowd are on the edge of their seats urging Arsenal to the end,
On Cup Final day.

Lehman to Lauren, Lauren to Campbell, Campbell to Cole, Cole chips
it to the captain
Delightful ball out to the wing
Where Pires collects it

Takes on the defender, cruises it to the back post
Could this be it? Reyes heads it back across the goal.

Charlie Carver (10)
Chiddingstone CE Primary School

Chelsea

Mourinho is the manager
Chelsea is the team
He won the FA Premier league and the Carling Cup
He gives Chelsea confidence
Even when they're down.

Mophead passed to Lampard
Lampard passed it back
Mophead took a might shot and knocked the goalie dead
Where was the defender when Mophead took the shot?
Half way out the stadium singing
'Raw Britannia, Britannia all the way
Three pork sausages and marmalade'.

John Sewell (9)
Chiddingstone CE Primary School

The Friend Who Never Looked Back!

My best friend ever
Was lost forever
When he went to a place called school
We said our goodbyes
Tears filled my eyes
This certainly wasn't cool!

He left in his car,
He drove, oh, so far
Past the bridge we both were scared of
I was starting school soon
To join in the gloom
That was what I wasn't aware of.

Tabitha Haysom (9)
Chiddingstone CE Primary School

The Fantasy

There are castles hovering over clouds of white cotton,
The air has a calm cool breeze
Dandelions are floating in the atmosphere
Constantly making you sneeze.

A great ball of fire hangs in the sky
Reflecting shades of pink
Roses are blooming everywhere
Helping your mind to think.

A sea of pure clean blue is there
With sea life weaving through
Like dolphins, coral and tropical fish
Always with something to do.

The locals around are jolly and crazy
But still try to keep clean
Sometimes they're relaxing and peaceful as well
Keeping the fantasy serene.

Aisha Bennett (11)
Chiddingstone CE Primary School

November Night Countdown

Ten fat sausages sizzling on the fire
Nine fiery flames reaching even higher.

Eight golden fountains fizzing in the dark
Seven glowing eyes whizzing across the park.

Six bright Catherine wheels spinning on the wall
Five red rockets twirling very tall.

Four tasty chestnuts roasting in a spoon
Three scary explosions covering the moon.

Two proud parents watching all the games
One lonely guy burning in the flames.

Phoebe Critchley (11)
Chiddingstone CE Primary School

My Dog, Duster

This poem is all about my dog
Who's black and white and furry
Sometimes he growls and barks a lot
Sometimes he's shy and girly.

Sometimes he jumps right over the gate
To come and play with me
Sometimes he runs off with my ball
And buries it under the tree.

Sometimes he follows me up the stairs
And hides underneath my bed
Sometimes he sneaks up in the mornings
And licks all over my head.

Sometimes he pinches my cottage pie
Which he knows is very wrong
Sometimes he pretends it wasn't him
And his eyes look sad and long.

Sometimes he chases the cat around
Who is really not impressed
Sometimes she turns and hisses at him
And shows him just who's best.

Sometimes I wish he'd leave me alone
When he wants me to throw his ball
But always, always I give in
Because I love him most of all.

Daniel Wiles (9)
Chiddingstone CE Primary School

My Cats

I have two cats, they're really nice
Although they hunt birds, rabbits and mice.

Pixie doesn't hunt that much
As she is nearly always sleeping
I pick her up and have a cuddle
And then she starts her weeping!
As Pixie is a scaredy-cat
She doesn't like people holding her
But maybe when she grows up
She will become a bit bolder.

Rhea takes life easy,
She goes to sleep in light,
She wakes up, full of energy,
Then she hunts for the night
Rhea's extremely friendly
She loves to have a hug
Although she can be disgusting
Because she'll eat so many bugs.

My cats hunt, they sleep and of course they eat
But, when they sleep, they're really sweet!
If I didn't have to hunt then I wish I were a cat!

Lindsey Hiscocks (11)
Chiddingstone CE Primary School

Time

T ime is a clever and strange thing
I t's something you can't change
M y time still goes on
E ven though it won't be long.

Harry Williams (9)
Chiddingstone CE Primary School

Love

Love is like a red rose bud blossoming in the breezy countryside
Love is the sound of a robin carolling in his creamy voice
Love is like a cherry pie, its taste strong and everlasting
Love is like the smell of summer and of spring flowers
Love is like a single red rose just bursting into bloom
Love is like a fluffy jumper which has been wrapped around my
                                                    beating heart.
Love is like the powerful feeling I've never known
Love is like my grandma holding me and my yellow chick before . . .
                                                    she died.

Eleanor Hodgett (11)
Chilton Primary School

Excitement!

Excitement is when the weekend starts and introduces relaxation!
Excitement is when you hear people's shouts of enjoyment from the
                                                    theme-park.
Excitement tastes lovely and active
Excitement smells delicious and irresistible
Excitement looks like people running about and everything moving
Excitement feels like you never want it to end.
Excitement reminds me of the time I had an endless water fight all day!

George Bates (11)
Chilton Primary School

Fear

Fear sounds like
The whisper of the wind
On a cold dismal night.

Fear tastes like
The salt of the sea
Burning on your tongue.

Fear smells like
Year old horse manure
Rotting in the straw.

Fear looks like
A silent headless ghost
Flowing through a silent graveyard.

Fear feels like
A World War II experience
In the dark feeling alone.

Fear reminds me of
Being trapped with a scary dummy
Telling me things I didn't want to know.

Fear is black, scary and dismal
My worst emotion
The emotion of dark.

Sophie Thomas (10)
Chilton Primary School

Fear

Fear is in a small box in your body
All waiting to be released by
Something that
Scares you.

Fear is a grey speck that
Grows and grows
It feels small then becomes big.

Fear is an emotion that everybody has
You hold inside you until
You're frightened.

Fear is something you can't get rid of
Sometimes you don't
Need to fear.

Joseph Lunn (10)
Chilton Primary School

Happiness

Happiness is pink like twinkling falling blossom
Happiness sounds like tweeting little birds
Happiness tastes like a smooth strawberry milkshake
Happiness smells like a pink flower full of scent
Happiness looks like a heart of gold pumping in your body
Happiness feels like a furry, silky pillow.

Lauren Stanley (10)
Chilton Primary School

Love

Love is real like a romantic scarlet rose all alone in a vase
Love feels like a warm home, waiting for you after a long day's work
Love looks like a beautiful beach on an island nowhere to be found
Love tastes like a huge milkshake flowing down your throat as smooth
as babies' skin.
Love sounds like the sweetest song playing over and over for as long
as the day will let it.
Love smells like the most attractive fragrance of a flower, picked
for the first time ever.
Love is everything sugary and nice, you can't imagine.

Danielle Aspital (11)
Chilton Primary School

Happiness

Happiness is green like summer leaves sparking in the sun light
Happiness sounds like birds tweeting in the tree tops
Happiness smells like lavender blowing in the breeze
Happiness tastes like candyfloss melting in your mouth
Happiness reminds me of getting my first medal at gymnastics
Happiness looks like somebody smiling.

Cherie-Alice Pointer (10)
Chilton Primary School

Anger

Anger sounds like someone screaming in agony
Anger tastes like the hottest chilli in the world
Anger smells like smoke coming from a bonfire
Anger looks like a bull rushing through a jungle
Anger feels like a shock going through a body
Anger reminds me of smashing glass against a wall
Anger is a colour of a dark red dripping down.

Daniel Gregory-Davis (10)
Chilton Primary School

Anger

Anger sounds like nails being scratched down a blackboard
Anger tastes like your mouth is getting washed out with soap
Anger smells like disgusting burning plastic
Anger looks like two cars having a dreadful car crash
Anger feels like you're being stabbed in the head
Anger reminds me of my two brothers beating me up
Anger is red like a dragon's fiery breath.

Lewis Luckhurst (10)
Chilton Primary School

Love

Love is blue like the sky at noon
Love sounds like the wind blowing into bottles.

It tastes as if chocolate is melting in your mouth
And smells like roses in a bush.

Love looks like a big shining heart
Love feels like warmness in my chest
And love reminds me of sweet apple pie.

Emilie Shaw (10)
Chilton Primary School

Happiness

Happiness is sugary sweets and small little ice cream
Happiness is little girls who are dancing
Happiness is a bunch of flowers in the summer breeze
Happiness is when everyone is being happy
Happiness is when people are smiling and never sad
Happiness is a very happy feeling
Happiness is pink, purple, blue, yellow.

Stephanie Alexandrou (10)
Chilton Primary School

Anger

Anger boiling up inside
Rearing up like a furious, cold-hearted bear
Roaring, roaring, roaring
I can't stop myself
Anger is controlling me
Twisting in my insides with rage
Like two armies, good and bad
Fighting to control
After the battle I'm left
Feeling sad and empty.

Yasmin Stubbings (9) & Richard Kennedy (10)
Chilton Primary School

Happiness

Happiness is when the weekend comes and there is no school
Happiness is when you have friends to play with
Happiness is when someone is nice to you
Happiness is like the sun shining in the sky
Happiness is like my favourite colour, pink
Happiness is when I go round my best friend's house
Happiness is when I have got my three best friends
Megan, Savannah and Eleanor.

Rebecca Offen (11)
Chilton Primary School

Anger

Anger is a bold red like a bright flashing danger alarm
Anger sounds like a fierce, roaring, fire-breathing dragon
Anger tastes like red-hot chilli
Anger smells like burning rubble from a bombed mansion
Anger looks like a fiercer fire than the Great Fire of London
Anger feels like your body rotting in boiling hot ashes
Anger reminds me of my mum's deep shouting voice.

Adam Topping (9)
Chilton Primary School

Darkness

Darkness is the black silhouette of the midnight sky as the sun creeps
away for the beginning of the moon.
It sounds silent and mystic like a lonely shadow haunting the night.
All you can feel is the cool brush against your skin of the hazy
midnight breeze.
When you taste darkness it's like a bitter, dry mixture of the rough
dust from the cold, hard pavements.
You can smell the spiteful wrought iron as you carry on past the rusty,
metal gates.
Darkness reminds me of a great light-striking storm.

Savannah Turner (10)
Chilton Primary School

Darkness

Darkness is when you feel like you're isolated in one space
Darkness is at night when you go to sleep and the big moon beams
in the sky
Darkness reminds me of camping out on a summer's night
Darkness tastes like fizzy Coca-Cola
Darkness smells like runny chocolate running down your throat
Darkness sounds like a big bang of black.

Holly Hill (11)
Chilton Primary School

Silence

Silence makes me feel dull
Silence is like walking through a town with nobody around
When I think of silence it reminds me of space
Then I think of deaf people and how it's like for them
Not to hear the trees blow or the sound of the ocean's waves
Crashing onto the wet sand and thinking . . .
What if I were deaf?

Charlie Lane (11)
Chilton Primary School

Darkness Is . . .

Darkness is when I can't see my feet, about to take their first step
in the ocean
Darkness is when we gat an unexpected blackout and I can't see
where I am or what I'm doing
Darkness is when I'm laying in bed, watching a blank screen, whilst
the sun goes down
Darkness is when I hug my dad and hide my head in his T-shirt
Darkness is when Mum's long wavy hair pokes me in the eye and
I can't see
Darkness is when someone's blind and shall never see again
Darkness is when people from extremely poor countries, die
from hunger
Darkness is when I blink and everything goes dark for a second
Darkness is when Jeremy and Amy are on, in hide-and-seek and
I hide in a wardrobe.
Darkness is when I'm upset and hide myself in the covers
Darkness is when Jeanie says goodnight to me and turns my light out
Darkness is when I die and I've got nothing to look forward to
Darkness is when there's no future.

Amanda Grigor (11)
Chilton Primary School

Silence

Silence is a pitch-black graveyard all quiet and still
Silence is nothing, like no one's there
Silence is eating a plain sponge cake which is really bland
Silence is so strong, so sweet but nothing can smell it
Silence is the most beautiful thing
But no one has ever seen it
Silence is the soft chilling breeze tickling your neck
Silence reminds me of meeting someone new and not knowing what
to say.

Katherine Denton (11)
Chilton Primary School

Anger, Anger!

Anger, anger like fire in your chest
Anger, anger like a demon inside you
Anger, anger like jumping through a ring of fire
Anger, anger the sourness of a lemon.

Anger, anger like a demon controlling you
Anger, anger someone picking on you and your eyes are so wet
with rage.

Anger, anger so rough and so tough
Anger, anger you stab and stab till death!

Joe Wheeler (11)
Chilton Primary School

Hate!

Hate sounds like a volcano just about to erupt
Hate tastes like hot lava sizzling and erupting inside your mouth as
you are getting angry
Hate smells really deep, horrible, hot, you can smell it from
a long distance
Hate looks angry, fierce and really tough
Hate you feel strong and you want to lash out at someone
Hate reminds you of yourself when you get angry.

Sam Goldfinch (11)
Chilton Primary School

Anger

Anger is like a hyena screaming in your head.
Anger is like tasting your own bitter blood, through your nose.
Anger is like the smell of bitter envy on your successor.
Anger is like seeing the Devil's lair up close.
Anger is like the blood in your head bubbling up until it blows.
Anger is when you lose to a cheating opponent.

Joe Holness (11)
Chilton Primary School

Love

Love, there only two girls in my life
I wish everyone of them could be my wife.
Firstly, there's Kate, she's great, I really hope she's my fate,
She's the only one who can conceal my hate.
Then there's Amanda, I can't think of anything to rhyme with her name
But I do love her, she's brilliant and beautiful.

Love leaves you feeling great, like an emotional volcano erupting,
                                        making you feel brilliant.

It sounds exotic or human, even the word is exquisite.
It tastes sweet and fresh
It smells like flowers, roses, even though they don't smell too nice
                                        it looks like it.
It feels brilliant, romantic, emotional, perfect.

Danny Harris (11)
Chilton Primary School

Love!

Love is the colour baby pink
Love is like the sound of someone you care for
Love tastes like chocolates covered in smooth caramel
Love smells like fresh lavender
Love looks like a pumping heart beating really fast
Love feels like somebody's hand smooth all around them.

Emma Bull (11)
Chilton Primary School

Sadness

Sadness is when your heart just breaks
Sadness is when you get a shock of pain
In the back of your throat when you're about to break down and cry
Sadness makes you feel small like you're an ant about to be squashed
Sadness makes you feel cold and empty inside.

Laura Phillips (11)
Chilton Primary School

Anger

Anger is a bomb inside you
Ready to explode

Anger is like someone poisoning you
When you are all alone.

Anger is an old house
Burning down slowly.

Anger is a volcano erupting
Wiping out every living thing around it.

Anger is fire burning around you
Getting nearer and hotter.

Anger is when happiness no longer exists inside you
And a thousand daggers going into your back,
And never stopping going in and out.

Louis Sarraf (11)
Chilton Primary School

Anger

Anger is dangerous and red
Storming around in my head
Making a raging roar
Like a giant boar
I fell, falling from a cliff
My worst enemy
Anger, anger, anger!

Kerry-Anne Huntlea (9)
Chilton Primary School

Anger

Anger swirling and jumping in my brain
Leaping on all my friends near
Colours so black and so red in its power
Changing into the softness that lay here
I feel so small now
I've lost all my friends
All because of my thinking.

Anger is bullying me
Stabbing me and saying,
'Go on, go on'
All of a sudden I am sad, fading away into my small soul
But then it whispers,
'Let's kill, let's kill'.

Anger! Anger! Anger!
Help me, I'm stuck
In my own little world
Living with this anger
Lightning and storm breaking
Inside of me forever!

Anger crashing on so sudden
So quick
Swallowing me up like a humongous giant
Mountains of burning fire
Splurting out and melting so quickly.

Natalie Dicks (10)
Chilton Primary School

Love

Love is a beautiful site
Love sounds like romance
Love smells like a red rose
Scented around the house
Love makes me feel like
A beautiful butterfly.

Jasmine Sarraf (11)
Chilton Primary School

Anger

Anger is a cold, dark and damp world
Where bad memories swallow you into Hell
We take our feelings out on everyone else
As we're dying inside.

It feels as if a knife goes through your soul
Red rage spurting out
A life of devastation eating you up
Making you feel like a dot.

A deadly, murderous fire
Pushing me further and further
Pushing me past the limit
Making my hair turn to fire.

Matthew Waller (9)
Chilton Primary School

Anger

Too hungry to fight
Trembling inside
Anger sharp like a knife
Eyes small
Shimmering like fire
Burning in my head
Can't get it out
Anger, anger, anger
Feeling empty
Freezing cold inside
Heart beating so fast
Feels like it's going to explode
Feeling distraught.

Kimberley Bottomley & Tonie Stroud (10)
Chilton Primary School

Anger

Anger is a feeling burning inside
And if you do something there is nowhere to hide
Anger is burning everywhere
And after I am left so bare.

Anger is sharp like dagger
It is red-hot rage bursting out
Anger destroying and extinguish away
And then there is nothing left to say.

Anger pounding red-hot rage through my heart
And it is so hurtful and hot
I just really got
Anger roaring and burning inside
And then I know where to hide.

Anger is red-hot rage
Every minute it is killing every page
I will never forget
The time I went red raging hot.

The rage and anger did hit
The thing that I always had,
And I sent it graving into a pit,
It had fire roaring inside, killing you.

Anger crushing and killing your head
After, you just feel you are dead.

Jamie Gregory-Davies (10)
Chilton Primary School

Love!

Love is red, it's as bright as a blazing fire
Love feels like it's warm inside your heart making you feel happy
It looks like a big bundle of red bullets floating inside your blood
It tastes like poisonous roses, the colour and texture
It smells like strawberry juice from real strawberries, squeezed
Love sounds like romance.

Demi Swan (11)
Chilton Primary School

Anger

Anger is like a soul inside you
Deep beneath the skin's crust
A red dragon ready to set fire to your heart.

An emotion that can't be controlled,
A never-ending pit.

Nothing can extinguish it,
Nothing can force it out
No one can burn it off with love.

Gnashing through your veins
Gushing like a whirlpool in your head.

Crushing all your self esteem
Drowning into the pits of Hell.

Roaring like an enormous fire
Ready to burn you, burn you, burn you . . .

Lewis Carter (10)
Chilton Primary School

Anger

Anger, anger, anger
Anger is hard to control
It makes me explode
Anger will never die out.

Anger, anger, anger
It makes me feel all threatened
It burns through my head like a storm
My heart beat's faster and faster.

Anger, anger, anger
It is red-hot rage in your soul
Anger is a light in you
It drowns you with frustration.

Samuel Graham (10)
Chilton Primary School

War

I watch from the our trenches looking into the mist
though expecting nothing
I can hear them, the mud squelching beneath their feet
A bomb falls in the distance and I hear screams
I shudder as I think of my family back home
I look back over the high trench wall, I see them
First fifty, then hundreds, they're coming,
Through the darkness and mist
The others jump to the guns and wait
I look at the general waiting for the order, he nods
We start firing as all you can see is dust and bullet caps
flying through the air
The air clears and we see them fall
Then all is silent
The only thing heard is the hissing of the guns and
the thumping of our hearts
I look around me at the other tired soldiers
I feel hatred flooding through me
Hatred for this world, hatred for everything
Now I'm determined I will survive.

Francesca Baylis (10)
Cuxton Junior School

Sadness!

Sadness is white like an apple, not ripe to eat
It sounds like nothing when you're cooped up in a cage
It tastes of air, it tastes like nothing
It smells like the sea when it has too much salt in it
It looks like a small stream, flooding into an ocean
It feels like an invisible ball, pushing you away from something you
love
It reminds me of a person crying to make a river
Someone's sadness is never complete, there is always a hint of
happiness.

Bethany Ainge (10)
Cuxton Junior School

The Desert

I can see the endless sand dunes
Mounting up before me like a great army
And the massive termite mounds
Taller than anything in the barren landscape
There is enough sand for the world's population to lie down on.

I can hear the gusting of the strong wind
Scattering thousands of grains of sand
And the pitter-patter of lizards' feet
Faintly against the crunching of mine
Above all the panting of my heavy breath.

I can feel a dry sensation in my mouth
Like a great lake, drained of its water
And the weight of my rucksack
Pulling me backwards
As the beads of sweat trickle down the back of my neck
I can feel the beating sun
Applying pressure to my body
As the pain of loneliness eats at my heart.

Michael McAdam (11)
Cuxton Junior School

Happiness

I can see a hot, sunny day with children laughing and playing around
I can hear people crying with laughter and enjoying themselves
I can feel happiness in people's hearts as they skip around
I can smell roses as they grow in the blazing sun
I can taste sugary strawberries as the juice touches my tongue
I hope for the people who are enemies, to be friends
I dream of the wind blowing and everything will be ripe, like the fruit on
the trees.

Amy Rodway (11)
Cuxton Junior School

FIFA Street!

I can see the ball being saved by the keeper
Like a bullet bouncing off steel.

I can feel the crowds cheering,
It sounds like a bomb exploding in the air.

I can hear the piercing whistle of the ref
It sounds like a screaming firework.

I can see the ball fly through the air
Like a comet orbiting Earth.

I can see the players passing the ball
On a pitch made of steel.

I can see the player as he lines up to take a penalty
But misses.

I can see a player on the run with the ball
He scores!

I can see the team celebrate as they win the match.

Lewis Wright (10)
Cuxton Junior School

Love

Love is red like a big red balloon,
It sounds like bells ringing as I kill
It tastes like a big white wedding cake
It smells like strawberry dipped in sugar
It looks like a big, bright red heart
It feels like smooth soft pillows
It reminds me of a feeling I never had before.

Sophie Weeden (10)
Cuxton Junior School

Soldier

I can see the first tear trickle down my mum's face as I greet her
goodbye
I'm in war now, I will treasure this moment forever
All I can hear is the wind rustling through the trees
I feel nothing then I feel pain as I got a shove from the colonel telling
me to move on
I dream for the war to be over as soon as it can
I hope for my family to be safe and calm
It's over now, I can smell the sweet smell of justice
I can still taste the mud from my head being buried in the ground.

Sam Martin (10)
Cuxton Junior School

Love!

Love is red like a big school, Cuxton fleece
Love sounds like a volcano erupting with lava coming out of the top
It tastes like strawberry bubble gum blowing bubbles and popping
It smells like strawberries dipped into sugar.
It looks like a big, bright balloon, the shape of a heart
It feels like smooth, soft cushions and butterflies in your tummy
It reminds me of a feeling that I had never had before.

Bria Bennett (10)
Cuxton Junior School

Evacuee

My mum waves goodbye to me, where am I going?
I felt sick as the train left the station.
I heard the engine and the sounds of the tracks as we went over them
I looked out the window and I saw nature, I think I am in the
countryside, not the town.
I feel the vibration of the train and the next thing I know I was
somewhere different.
I hope my mum and dad are on the next train I dream I was in.

Rebecca Ostridge (10)
Cuxton Junior School

Love

Love sounds like laughter, singing and relaxing voices
It tastes like honey, sugar and sweet ripe pears
It smells like roses and jasmines swaying in the wind
Love looks like a light glowing with a gentle pink
It feels like silk, smooth and cool, but warm when you need it
It reminds me of caring and helping people,
You feel nice to have a friend
Love makes you feel warm and glad to be part of the world
It's like a new world with happiness and joy
It makes the world a better place and no one can take
                          your happiness away.

Yasmin Ali (10)
Cuxton Junior School

Hate Is . . .

Hate is black like an angry panther
It sounds like an 800-year-old oak tree falling to the ground
It tastes like horrible broccoli, a big one
It smells like a big explosion of petrol
It looks like a big bolt of lightning
It feels like the prickly spikes of a hedgehog
It reminds me of thick red blood.

Ellie Webber (10)
Cuxton Junior School

Soldier

I can see huge boats shining their way through the sea
A door zooming down from the boat and people rushing onto shore
I can hear the flames crackling in the distance
The mud splashing as we go in to battle
I can hear fires out of guns
I can feel a heavy pack on my back, weighing me down and the
Sadness from all the lives lost.

Joshua Linares Stanley (10)
Cuxton Junior School

Soldier!

I can see bombs exploding in the air and making puddles of mud
I can see my men shifting themselves to safety
I can hear the raindrops dropping on my helmet and I can hear people
Screaming for help, because they are hurt
I can feel the cold, wet water soaking through my clothes
And I feel homesick and afraid
I can smell smoke and smell of disgust
Because people are trying to harm me
I can taste food from my last meal, which I think will be my last
I hope to see my family again
I dream of being home with my family and not in the war I am in.

Cameron Fryer (10)
Cuxton Junior School

Silence

Silence is calm and brilliantly bright
Tastes like whipped cream, deliciously white
Smells like red roses
Sounds like crunching in snow
Looks like the horizon, beginning to glow
Silence is a mouse and also a dove
It's also a symbol of kindness and love.

Ellen Le Brunn & Kate Brown (11)
Cuxton Junior School

What Is Love . . . ?

Love sounds like the feathery doves, singing in the sunny wet dew
It tastes like creamy milk chocolate, that melts in your mouth
It smells like the woody flowers in the mossy woods
It feels like a big brown teddy bear sitting on a snugly bed
It looks like a wet petal off the deepest red rose
It reminds me of a yellow bright sunny day with clouds drifting through
the sky.

Emily Martin (10)
Cuxton Junior School

The Beach Of Happiness

I feel soft, warm sand
Weaving in and out of my toes
Everyone is laughing and cheering
As they play games in the blazing sun
I hear the sea is always talking to everyone
As it laps up pebbles and takes them into the depths of his land
I see colourful, bright beachballs
Being tossed around in the happy atmosphere
And the gentle breeze
Still rustling through my hair.

Samantha Mussellwhite (11)
Cuxton Junior School

The Soldier

Fear is climbing up inside of me
As I'm hiding in the mud sinking ditch
The Nazi cross is burning through me
Guiltily I point my gun at a soldier
Trying hard to pull the trigger
Whilst all I can hear is screaming and crashing bombs
All I can see is people
Rushing to their bomb shelters to safety
But no matter where I go
Or what I say, it always feels like something is watching me.

Jessica Chatfield (11)
Cuxton Junior School

Competing Against The Professionals

As I jump onto the beam
I feel the pressure, knowing I need to win
I feel the cold surface of the mat sticking to my sweaty feet
I can feel my nerves shivering up my spine.

As I stand upon the beam I hear my supporters cheering me on
I hear the creaking of the beam as I press my weight against it
As I begin to see my coach miming, 'You can do it'
I see the pros warming up knowing they're the best.

As I step up to 1st place on the stand
I know I'm the *best!*

Olivia Cobley (10)
Cuxton Junior School

Love . . . ?

Love is full of colours and surprises
It feels softer than a cloud
It smells finer than the sweetest perfume
More gentle than the smell of flowers in bloom,
It looks better than anyone could ever imagine.
Even in a dream
Love is easy to find
It is always somewhere
Just a few steps ahead of you
Love is the greatest feeling.

Leila da Cunha Soares (11)
Cuxton Junior School

Love

Love sounds like
Angels playing on a harp
While you sit next to a pond
Looking at the carp.

Love tastes like Turkish delight
So sweet it makes you drool at first sight

Love smells like the sweetest rose
Watered by can and watered by hose.

Love looks like a peaceful dove
Flying through the skies of blue above.

Love feels like a piece of silk
So soft, it feels liquid like milk.

Olivia Guechtoum (10)
Cuxton Junior School

Anger

Anger feels like a fire
Burning in my heart
It sounds like thunder
Hammering in my ears
It reminds me of lightning
Electric from the start
It smells like smoke
Clotting up my mind
It tastes like chillies
Stinging in my mouth
It looks like a charging bull
Chasing me from behind.

Oliver Watts (11)
Cuxton Junior School

Football Fever!

The piercing noise of the ref's whistle
Sounds like a comet whizzing through the sky

The crowds chanting sounds like an
Earthquake rumbling throughout the earth.

I can feel the vibrations as the
Crowd cheer their team on.

I can see all the players playing
Proudly in the stadium of glory.

I can feel the pressure on the
Penalty taker as he shoots at goal.

I can see the celebrations as the
Penalty taker's team celebrate.

Jack Harper (10)
Cuxton Junior School

The Trench Below

They called me in to the trench below
Where I sat and heard the gunshots flow
Is this really going on I thought?
But I have no time, so I just shot.
To protect my country, my freedom, my liberty
For that matter, I must fight, try my best
Just like the soldiers and all the rest.

Morgan Cooke (11)
Cuxton Junior School

The Helpless Slave

The pressure is on as the beam of the sunlight heat grows stronger.
Aching slaves reaching their limit to complete the tomb
                                        as the Pharaoh arrives.
Farmers harvesting crops unaware of the Nile flooding endlessly
                                        across the land.

It is a chaotic atmosphere as the Pharaoh arrives to inspect the tomb.
Pain is spinning up my spine as the Nile thunders through the food
                                        and crops.
I feel helpless as the Pharaoh destroys the tomb and the Nile
                                        continues to flood.
I can hear the panting breaths of slaves as they lay on the ground
                                        in fear.
I can hear the screaming and yelling of children and adults dashing
                                        from the flood.
The giggle of my family, assures me that everything will be alright.

Samantha Rankin (11)
Cuxton Junior School

Blackpool, But What Is The Big One?

It sounds loud as it carries me down
It's like the birds are whispering in my ear
The waves are like thunder, as the rocks push them away.

I feel the tracks go click, click, click as it carries me on
I felt the rain trickle down my nose
The north Liverpool wind was blowing in my ear.

I see the fire-red tracks as I go down
I saw the shimmering calm Irish sea
As it tipped me up I saw the baby blue sky.

As the ride ends, I see my family down below
But now you know *the big one!*

Kitty Porter (9)
Cuxton Junior School

Love

Love sounds like calming classical music
Slowly slithering into my ears
Love tastes like chocolate with caramel
Satisfying my taste buds with a rich creamy sensation
Love smells like a freshly picked rose
Blooming brightly with a sweet calming aroma
Love looks like a pink heart
Dancing around my body
Love feels like a cool, soft silk cushion
That relaxes you when you lay down to relax
Love reminds me of a cat sleeping
Gently purring in a calm rest.

Sally Burrows (11)
Cuxton Junior School

Anger

The sound of anger is sizzling
Like sausages in a pan frying
Anger tastes like chillies burning in my mouth
The smell is strong and smoky
Like the smoke fuming out of a train's funnel
I can see power in the anger
Like when lions fight
Anger feels rough
Like sandpaper as it rubs against you
Anger reminds me of the colour red
Like an exploding volcano.

Lauren Speirs (11)
Cuxton Junior School

Love

Love sounds like a buzzing bee
Buzzing around you and me
Love tastes like bubblegum ice cream
It will make you calm and you won't scream
Love smells so sweet and sugary
I ask why love won't come to me
Love looks like a little red light
That makes you go to sleep at night
Love feels so gentle and calm
Like putting on your lip balm
Love reminds me of a red rose
That makes your eyes want to close.

Billie Watkins (10)
Cuxton Junior School

A Soldier In The War

I feel the rain bouncing off my helmet
I hear the guns roaring
I see the magazine in men's guns

I feel the vibration on the ground
I hear the tank's engine roaring
I see the cannons firing at me

I feel the pain rushing through my body
I hear the men shouting for cover
I see black dots in the sky, I think they must be planes

Who will win this mighty war?

Josh Marden (9)
Elham CE Primary School

A Soldier In The War

What can you see?
I can see the explosions killing thousands of people
The tanks rumbling around me
I can see bullets shooting holes in people
Tanks blasting down walls.

What can you feel?
I can feel my gun clutched in my sweaty hands
The pain spreading slowly from my leg
I can feel the slippery mud under my feet
The tanks flattening the ground.

What can you hear?
I can hear the guns pelting their bullets at people
I can hear the generals shouting orders at their troops
The screams of men in pain
I can hear the planes overhead.

Bobby Andrews (8)
Elham CE Primary School

The War

The guns firing, bombs exploding
The war has started

Bodies lying everywhere
Machine gun firing into the air
The war has started

I can feel tanks rumbling
Our men running
The war has started

Death in the air
My rifle in my hand
The war has started.

James Brookes (9)
Elham CE Primary School

A Soldier In The War

I see . . .
Bomb erupting on the ground
Grenades exploding
Tanks coming towards me
Dead soldiers on the shaky ground.

I feel . . .
Vibrations from the floor
A shiver in my spine
Maggots coming out of my wound
And pleased I'm not dead.

I hear. . .
Soldiers screaming to death
Exploding bombs
Echoing trenches
And guns shooting.

Jake Theoff (9)
Elham CE Primary School

A Soldier In The War

What do you see?
I see
Dead bodies falling and hitting
The ground

What do you feel?
I feel a long
Pain in my weak body
All around

What do you hear?
I hear bombs
Dropping and exploding
Which is a noisy sound.

Sam Roud (9)
Elham CE Primary School

A Marine In The Navy

What did you see?
I saw ships sinking
People in the water struggling to cling on for life
Ships blazing, on fire in the night sky.

What did you feel?
I felt as if I were going to get hit by a torpedo
I felt nervous
I thought that I would not make it back.

What did you hear?
I heard screams as members of my crew yelped in pain
I heard planes up ahead
I heard explosions as boat by boat they sank to
The depths of the ocean.

Darwin Hamilton-Radford (10)
Elham CE Primary School

A Soldier In The War

I hear planes crashing down in the distance
I see bombs exploding outside of the trench
I feel mud and blood blow in my feet
I smell poisonous gas inside the trench
I see a soldier outside the trench in pain
I smell blood in the trench going everywhere
I feel bodies under my feet
I hear guns firing into the air.

Sophie Peers (8)
Elham CE Primary School

A Soldier In The War

What can you see?
I can see the Germans, their guns at my face
The smell of gunpowder drifting up my nostrils
As they load their guns it starts to rain
I feel this is the end of my life

What can you hear?
I heard the gunfire of my friends
Some of them screaming with pain
Falling to the ground, the land
Starts to shake as I see planes diving and swooping

I pray that someone would shoot them down
Our men are falling and dying
With blood stained wire all over
The trigger was pulled and I was gone.

Bradley Andrews (8)
Elham CE Primary School

A Soldier At War

What can you see?
I can see soldiers on the hill
Charging at me one by one
Bullets flying
Soldiers crying

What can you hear?
Soldiers crying someone's hurt
Bullets landing in the dirt
Bombs crashing, the turf smashing

What can you feel?
The blood is no longer at my heart
I am weak, blind, homesick - *dead!*

Sophie Bennett (9)
Elham CE Primary School

A Soldier In The War

What can you see?
I see men lying where they fell
I see smoke where guns have fired
I see men running and fighting for their lives
I see shells falling all around me.

What can you hear?
I hear shells exploding
I hear the cries of men
I hear guns firing
I hear my heart beating.

What can you feel?
I feel the gas close in
I feel my terrified body moving
I feel the squishy mud around me.

James Hirst-Beecham (9)
Elham CE Primary School

A Soldier In The War

What can you see?
I can see bomb shells falling from the planes hitting
The ground and blowing up buildings.

What can you hear?
I can hear army men yelling and grenades blowing up
Things all around as bombs hit the ground.

What can you feel?
The barrel of my gun bullets rattling in my pocket the
Itching of my uniform the squelch of the mud.

Tim Astbury (8)
Elham CE Primary School

A Soldier In The War

What can you see?
I can see the cranes shifting crates into the enormous ships
I can see U-boats floating in the docks
People in their homes locking their locks.

What can I feel?
I feel as scared as an antelope running away from a lion
I am almost dead, the explosions are loud
And the feeling I have is horrible.

What can I hear?
I can hear the bombs landing on the buildings
I can hear the guns firing bullets.
I can hear people screaming and then the buildings explode
As the ships carry their loads.

Joshua Blackford (9)
Elham CE Primary School

The Soldiers' War

Tired soldiers huddle so they can live
Planes crashing over their heads
They are sleepy, they fight day and night

They are tired, sad and brave
They fight for me and you
They die for me and you.

Rebecca Allen (9)
Elham CE Primary School

A Soldier In War

What can you see?
I can see tears in the soldiers' eyes
Wishing they had not said so many lies
Knowing they could soon lose their lives
Clinging to pictures of their children and wives.

What can you feel?
I feel a chill down my spine
As planes fly over ahead
My gun in my hand feels as cold as lead
The person next to me is dead.

What can you hear?
I can hear the dripping blood
Hear men falling with a thud
Falling on the soaking mud
Never going to get up.

Alice Olsson (8)
Elham CE Primary School

A Soldier In The War

What can you see?
I can see blood scattered around the dead bodies in front of me.

What can you feel?
I can feel slimy mud slipping down like a flea.

What can you hear?
I can hear the crying of pain and the trembling ground
                              beneath my knee.

Connor Loome (9)
Elham CE Primary School

A Soldier In The War

What can you feel?
I can feel my bloodstained stomach aching
As well as the hot metal of my rifle barrel
The rush of a bullet ripping past
The recoil of my gun against my shoulder

What can you hear?
I hear my gun exploding onto the German front line
Water splashing into muddy pools mixed with blood
I can hear the hiss of a smoke grenade
The trundle of a tank on its metal tracks

What can you see?
I can see death from one single finger
A grenade thrown by my own hand
The bullet studded tree marking no-man's-land
Dead people lying on the ground.

Fraser Nurse (9)
Elham CE Primary School

Soldier In The War

I can see bombs exploding, throwing people in the air.
I can hear bullets blasting in the earth.
I can feel pain rushing through my body.
I can see planes crashing down and killing.
I can hear the lightning screeching in the distance.
I can feel death creeping up my back.
I can see burnt trees collapsing, German warriors.
I can hear women screaming, dying in my head.
I can feel the sweat on my rich-black gun.

Abby Moffatt
Elham CE Primary School

If Gymnastics Was Easy They'd Call It Football

When you're on the bar you need a lot of grip
For if you don't have the grip you're sure to slip
Swing around the bar like you're queen of the air
But remember to take a lot of care
On the beam it takes a lot of balance
When you have the balance you can show off your talents
Along the beam do flips and jumps
With a cracking dismount that ends in a crunch!
On the vault you run your fastest and jump and spring, neatly land
Present to judges, turn and then go back and start you run again
Tackle the floor with a fantastic tumble
Be careful it doesn't end in a crumble
Choose the music you want to dance to
And show the judges what you can do
Then at the end the time you spend waiting to come first? Or second?
Fingers crossed and breath held tight
Will your score count? Well it just might!

Ellie Wyatt (8)
Haddon Dene School

The Playground's Wind

The playground's a loud garden with children's laughter and play
They like to swing on the monkey bars and land on the swing
They jump off and land down to the ground
Suddenly they're as quiet as a mouse
They glide down the twirly slide
And run around like lunatics
They fall on the ground, they bump their heads and cry with sorrow
The teacher comes and hears 'boo hoo!'
And puts ice on their heads.

Charlotte Stirling (9)
Haddon Dene School

Massive Machines

They're big, they're small
They're fat and tall
They're long or short
They come in all different sizes
And they're massive machines.

They're shiny, they're dull
They're dark, they're bright
They're yellow and green
They're dirty or clean
They come in all different colours
And they're massive machines.

They're smelly and noisy
They rattle and shake
They're ever so fast
And you then have to brake
They come with all different engines
And they're massive machines.

They pull, they shove
They dig and heave
They lift or carry
And some even weave
They do all different things
And they're massive machines.

From tractors to cranes
To tanks and trains
And boats and planes
They have all different names
And are massive machines.

Jerome Edridge (9)
Haddon Dene School

Food

If there's one thing in life
That's plain to me
It's everyone likes food
Be it junk or healthy.

There's different reactions
To be had from each type
From 'brain freeze' by ice cream
To the sourest taste
Of grapes that aren't ripe.

Some eat onions like apples
And lemons like they're sweet
Sprouts as if they enjoy them
And cabbage as a treat.

Me, well I love pasta
A big plateful for tea
My idea of Heaven
Is glorious spaghetti.

Matthew Speed (9)
Haddon Dene School

The Silly Dog

There is a dog as silly as a bone
Although I think he is
I climbed on to the fence
To see if he is
He was bashing his head on the fence
I thought to myself,
What a silly dog
Must be life, I guess.
Don't you think?

Phoebe Sola (9)
Haddon Dene School

Doomsday

The school seemed dead
I realised that nearly every face was full of dread
Only four had a look of happiness near
Everyone else was full of fear
I was sorry for one boy
For no toys could cease the endless torrent of tears
Streaming down to the ground
All playtime I hid
I hid as if I was under a dustbin lid
Finally the day came to its end
The torture had at last stopped
But what did my mum tell me?
Back again tomorrow!

Rowan De Bues (10)
Haddon Dene School

Holidays

H appy children playing in the pool
O pen sea shining from the sun
L aughter all around us
I   n the sea lilos float
D ays are long and lots of fun
A nd dolphins are frolicking
Y our parents are snoring
S unset is coming to me.

Bronwyn Yeoman (9)
Haddon Dene School

My Dog

My dog is lovely and tiny and sweet
Especially when he's asleep on my feet
He has long hair all shiny and white
When he's been in the mud it's such a sight
All muddy and messy and very smelly
Like animals in the jungles, I see on the telly
When my dog's good, I give him treats
Like my big juicy bones, he likes to eat
Sometimes he buries them in the flowers
The one Mum's been planting for hours and hours
But she doesn't mind at the end of the day
He's one of the family, we all say.

Bethany Johnson (9)
Haddon Dene School

Flowers

I like flowers in the spring time
I like making daisy chains
Flowers smell sweet
And I can put them in my hair

Some are pink, some are blue
They come in all different colours
What I really like about them
Is that they grow in the garden.

Rebecca Johns (9)
Haddon Dene School

Hot Seating

I sat on the hot seat chair
I saw people who had a stare
I looked around the room
And thought whom
I should ask the first question

I asked Rebecca Rose
Who has red spots on her toes
She asked a question which was silly
So I decided to ask Millie
She said, 'How old are you?'
So I said to her, 'I am two.'
And that was the end of my turn
I was glad because the seat was making me burn.

Millie Harris (8)
Haddon Dene School

My Rabbit

He's grey and brown
He doesn't make a sound
I love him so much
He doesn't make me frown

He gets bigger every day
I hope he never runs away
If he did I'd be very sad
But also I'd be mad

I try to remember to close his hutch
But my little brother doesn't help very much
He tries to take my rabbit's carrot
And then he says, 'I want a parrot!'

Mollie Ramos (7)
Haddon Dene School

I Saw It!

I saw it in the playground
A snake! A snake! A snake!
I see it in the playground
They are planning to dunk me in the lake

I saw it in the classroom
A board rubber and ruler
I see it in the classroom
They are rubbing our
Homework off the board

I saw it in the changing room
People getting changed
I see it in the changing room
People of all different ages

I saw it in the school stables
They are going for a hack
I hear it in the school stables
I hope they come back.

Johanna Pearson-Farr (8)
Haddon Dene School

Sharks

Dog sharks are the spottiest sharks
Sting rays are the stingiest
Great whites are the predators
While baskings are the most big mouthed
Whale sharks are the bluest and the biggest
The most revolting are the ragged tooth sharks
With the most disgusting of teeth.

Charlie Cawdron (9)
Haddon Dene School

Roman Aromas

In far-off fifty-five BC
Julius Caesar arrived by sea
With lovely breath and Roman nose
Smelt just like a fragrant rose.

But then upon the beach they smelt
The odours of the smelly Celt
The Romans soon felt pretty sick
Was this a smelly Celtic trick?

The Romans found to their dismay
It really was to foul to say
The Brits were fierce their tribes were strong
And what was worse, the rotting pong.

Thierry Preston (8)
Haddon Dene School

Waterfalls

Wet water waterfalls
Rushing
Down
Lower and lower
Until. . .
Splash!
It hits the bottom
Washing everything away
Whoosh!
Everything is gone.

Josh Yeoman (8)
Haddon Dene School

The Sun

When the sky is blue
And the sun is bright
The flowers grow
And bees buzz around
Children play in the sunlight
All day and night
Flowers get bigger
With different colours appearing
Birds fly about
And sing their song
In the green trees
Where they sleep.

Lugain Rfidah (8)
Haddon Dene School

The Sun

The sun was rising
I was happy and smiling
What shall we do today?

Play in the pool
Build a sandcastle
Surfing in the sea

What a beautiful day it was
It was fun in the sun.

Harry Price (7)
Haddon Dene School

Ballet

The orchestra is about to start
Now it's time for me to take part

I spin and jump up onto the stage
Like a bird released from its cage

The audience watch with great interest
Because they think we are the best

We dance across the stage with ease
In pretty little groups of threes

The glistening costumes sparkle in the light
The crowd think we are an absolute delight

The show goes on and the curtains fall
We take our bow to one and all.

Gabriella Panteli (8)
Haddon Dene School

The Bee

Out in the garden what is that sound?
Buzz buzz buzzing all around
I'm curious to see what is in the tree
Could it be the bumblebee?

Look at the colours yellow and black
Look at the stripes spring on her back
Mummy it makes honey
Look and see the queen bee.

Grace Murray (7)
Haddon Dene School

Porridge

Sloppy, slimy, sticky porridge
Which my mummy makes me eat
It always bubbles in my tummy
For something horrible
I think I should have something yummy
Which melts in my tummy
That is called a chocolate bar
Yummy, yummy, yummy

Chocolate is the best
It's better than the rest
Porridge makes my tummy ache
Chocolate makes bubbles
Yummy, yummy, yummy

And now all I eat
Is chocolate
Instead of porridge
Yummy, yummy, yummy.

Jenny Dening (9)
Haddon Dene School

My Brother

My brother is a bit mad
And sometimes a bit bad

He never eats his dinner
So I am always the winner

He keeps me up at night
And always thinks he's right

He likes riding his bike
To give mummy a fright

But he is my brother
I wouldn't want another.

Daniel Jackson (8)
Haddon Dene School

The Jumping Boy With His Toy

The boy jumped here
The boy jumped there
In his hand he held a toy
He was a very happy boy!
But he screamed too loud
He yelled too high
He woke his mum and dad up
They had a headache
They told him off and smacked his bum

He screamed so loud it was so bad
He kicked their legs and ran to his room
He shouted, 'Nanny!'
His mum and dad had another headache!
He screamed too loud again!
Oh dear!

Melissa Brill (8)
Haddon Dene School

Flowers

Spring brings new life to flowers and all
Flowers smell lovely especially when picked
And put in a vase in the hall
In the summer when it's sunny and fine
The flowers lift their heads up to the sunshine
They also look great in the sunshine.

Kyri Papa-Adams (8)
Haddon Dene School

Fireworks

The dark night
The sizzling, colourful fireworks
The blazing heat of the bonfire

The misty air
The sparkling Catherine wheels

The loud bangs echoing through the smoky air
Everyone enjoys themselves on fireworks night

The shock on people's faces
As the guy stares down on us

The children messing around the bonfire
The bangs and crackles of fireworks.

Bradley Keens (10)
Haddon Dene School

Skipping

Skipping, skipping, skipping is so great
I like to skip every day

Skipping, skipping, skipping is so great
I like to skip at break

Skipping, skipping, skipping is so great
I skip to bed with a cake.

Bradley Jarman (8)
Haddon Dene School

You!

You!
Your nose is like a rose
You!
Your eyes are like glistening stars
You!
Your lips are like the centre of my heart
You!
Your cheeks are like blossom
You!
You're beautiful
You!
Your hair is like silk
You!
Your skin is like rosemary.

Emily Mitchell (8)
Haddon Dene School

My Family

F orgiving each other
A happy family
M aking each other feel special
I n everything you do
L oving and caring
Y ou know they're always there for you.

Giorgia Amato (10)
Haddon Dene School

Colours

Colours galore!
Colours over here
Colours over there
Red, yellow, blue and green
Lots of colours everywhere

Coloured books, coloured pens, coloured creatures
Red, yellow, blue and green
Coloured things everywhere

Orange, pink, brown and violet
There's millions of colours to be found
Lots of colours everywhere.

Connor Winter (9)
Haddon Dene School

Fairies

Red, blue, lilac and yellow
They were all pretty fairies
The red one liked to roam in the meadow
The blue one liked to eat Dairy Milk
The lilac one liked to run free in the forest
And the yellow one liked to wear yellow silk
Their names were
Lilly, Bella, Daisy, Marigold
Lilly was the red one
Bella was the blue one
Daisy was the yellow one
And Marigold was lilac.

Poppy Lawson (9)
Haddon Dene School

The Boy

There once was a boy
Who truly wanted his toys
He looked everywhere
But Lloyd could not find them

He went to his mum
And said, 'Where are my toys!'
'I gave them to Droid.'
'No! Not Droid!'

Droid was his little brother
Who broke everything
Next time, the boy thought
I'll sell them before Droid gets those toys.

Pierre Laurens (9)
Haddon Dene School

School

School is great, school is cool
My school is the greatest of all
Learning is made fun with geography and French
You can play it or have races to the bench
I don't know why school is so great
Maybe it's all the effort teachers make.

Charlie Mitchell (8)
Haddon Dene School

New Year's Day

N ow that it's New Year
E verybody celebrates and is full of joy
W onderful things happen like fireworks at night.

Y ellow, orange and purple they go shooting in the sky
E verybody's happy and have a countdown from 10 to 0
A uld Lang Syne is sung every new year
R esolutions are made at the beginning of each year
S treamers are everywhere, thrown about.

D ecember has passed and a new year has come
A nyone is invited to celebrate all night
Y early the new year tradition is continued, including this year, 2005.

Irzam Ahmed (11)
Haddon Dene School

Brian Had A New Motorbike

Brian's Kawasaki
Went as fast as
The wind
It was big, shiny and green
Everywhere he rode
He rode at speed
Me on the back as happy as can be!

Ryan Coleman (8)
Haddon Dene School

RNLI

The RNLI is the lifeboat institute
You will see them with their lifejackets and their big yellow boats
The lifeboats can be big or small, slow or fast to drive
But in all weathers, rain or snow, they can survive
As soon as there is an incident, a pager will beep
Because someone has called the coastguard and he has arrived in
his jeep
People have all kinds of accidents cause they think it's fun
But if you hurt yourself they won't know what to do and run
Also there are weaver fish you might think are cute
But when you tread on them and get poisoned, then you'll think
they are brutes!
They'll come to you at rivers, lakes and shores
But some people think that because they're volunteers, they're bores
So just because they don't get paid don't think they do it for fun
Because when you're in trouble, wherever you are, it's to the lifeboats
they run
So it doesn't matter where you are
They'll come to you, near or far.

Molly Hirst (11)
Haddon Dene School

My First Memories Of School

When I entered school there were children playing in the sand pool
Others inside making bricks with a tool

When I entered school, there were many children crying
While mums and dad stood sighing

When I entered the lunch hall, there were children short and tall
Sitting down waiting for the lunch call

When I entered the outside
I approached the children at the slide, all but one to ran to hide

His name was George Beadle .

Ashley Bourne (11)
Haddon Dene School

Fireworks And Bonfire Night

Sparkling, shooting fireworks
Going through the sky
Up to its highest reach and then
Bang!

Catherine wheels spinning, round and round
Smoke drifting in the air
The golden moon in the background in a black night.

The bonfire's raging with light
As you can smell the burning smell
Children eating toffee apples and enjoying themselves
Everyone is wrapped up warm
Staring into the fire.

Francesca Nadin (11)
Haddon Dene School

Stars

Stars, stars shiny and bright
Stars, stars shine at night

Stars are like a giant dot to dot
Which can never be solved
Stars, stars shine at night

Shooting stars, shiny stars, sparkling and twinkling
Stars, stars shine at night.

Charlie Cragg (8)
Haddon Dene School

The Seasons

S unshine is here again bringing the
P romise of new life
R oses, daffodils, snowdrops and crocuses start to flower
I n the fields there are lambs frolicking around
N ests are filled up with lots of eggs, and the
G rass is green and bright.

S corching summer is here again. 'Let's go surfing,' I say
U mbrellas up, beach huts too
M y ice cream is melting in the brightly coloured sun
M y friends and I like to go in the beautiful, sparkly sea
E leanor and I are sailing our rubber dinghy
R elaxing in the cool, shimmering sea is my favourite.

A pple bobbing and trick or treating is great at Hallowe'en
U mbrellas blown inside out by the blustery winds
T hat send the leaves fluttering to the ground
U nder the dry bed of leaves there lie shiny conkers
M isty morning with dew on the grass
N uts gathered by cheeky red squirrels.

W inter I think is the best season of the year
I cy, cold days tobogganing down the hill
N uts roasting on the brightly coloured fire
T hick, white snow falling from the dull, grey sky
E xcited children writing letters to Santa
R oads filling up with white crunchy snow.

Tessa Dening (11)
Haddon Dene School

Morning Birds

As the morning wakes
The birds all fly
Across the sunrise
And the deep blue sky
They stretch their wings out wide
As they fly with pride
Across the sunrise
And in the morning glide.

There are thousands of birds
That glide and swoop
And maybe do a loop-the-loop
Perching on the tree tops high
And on the roof of coloured houses
The breeze is cold
So the birds have to snuggle up warm
To protect their newborn.

Jennifer Pearson-Farr (11)
Haddon Dene School

Fireworks

We walk down the town to the beach
To see the beautiful fireworks

When we get there
We see emerald green spirals in the air

Crackle, bang, fireworks go in the cold night

Some of the fireworks go off at such a height

I asked my dad if I could have a toffee apple from the man
My dad said, 'Of course you can.'

Ash floating down in the air landing everywhere
At the end of the display, all the people go away.

Dylan Mitchard (11)
Haddon Dene School

Dogs

Long-haired dogs
Short-haired dogs
All the funny little dogs

Big dogs
Small dogs
The cheeky little baby dogs

Playful dogs
Sleepy dogs
Eating all their food dogs

Clever dogs
Silly dogs
Sneaky catch the rabbit dogs

Lazy dogs
Lively dogs
Drive you round the bend dogs

Quiet dogs
Loud dogs
All the barking mad dogs

Smart dogs
Scruffy dogs
Mucking up your garden dogs

Naughty dogs
Sensible dogs
All the different types of dogs

Friendly dogs
Nasty dogs
All the brave and scared dogs

Cute dogs
Cuddly dogs
The dirty and the clean dogs.

Nicola Carter (9)
Ightham Primary School

Springtime

Leaves growing on the trees
No more mess for us to see
Leaves are turning bright green
And it makes a beautiful scene

Little birds all around
Mothers waiting on the ground
Baby birds need to learn
How to catch a wiggly worm

Rabbits nesting in the ground
Foxes hunting all year round
Hedgehogs coming out to play
Catching worms from day to day

Sunshine is coming
Cold is coming
Lovely day it will be
For the animals to see

Skipping through the meadow on a lovely day
It makes me feel so happy to watch the lambs play
They leap through the flowers, dancing as they go
Chasing one another and putting on a show.

Chloe Penfold (7)
Ightham Primary School

Autumn Time

Leaves orange, yellow and red
Falling into a bird's bed
Rabbits nesting in the ground
Coming up to play around

Squirrel climbing up a tree
What a view for it to see
Dormouse creeping to and fro
Getting ready for that awful snow

A pile of leaves on the ground
Some leaves pointy, some leaves round
As the day turns into dawn
The animals are trying to keep warm

Staring into silence, I cannot hear a sound
There's nothing but the scrunching of leaves on the ground
Bye-bye green leaves
Hello red leaves

Autumn time is here
And the rain and snow is near
I wish I could stay forever, but now I have to go
And leave behind the beauty of this splendid autumn show.

Karly Penfold (10)
Ightham Primary School

Summer

My neighbour's in the sun nearby
Birds are flying in the sky
Let's go and play outside
You can seek we will hide.

Colourful plants waving in the wind
All the dead flowers have been binned
I'm so hot, let's get cool
Who's the first in the pool?

Never mind you got there first
Don't make the rubber ring burst!
Go and get Dad
He thinks we're really mad.

Lovely barbecue for lunch
With salad and French bread to crunch
Never mind I fell over
In the long grass and clover.

Get up to bed!
Guess what I said
I can't get to sleep
The sun will never keep.

Alice Watson (8)
Ightham Primary School

The Day That School Closed Early!

The day that school closed early I was left behind
All the teachers had gone home, they're never really kind

I started to do my homework, but I couldn't find help
I heard a noise, a weird one, it sounded like a yelp

A vision of white wrapped up in mist
It came into the classroom it looked, it hissed

It walked slowly in its rags and tatters
Then it said, 'There's nothing to homework that really matters.'

I was frightened, frightened as can be
It took me by the hand and said, 'Let me help thee.'

I handed in homework I got an A*
If it wasn't for that vision I wouldn't have got so far.

Honey McElhill (11)
Ightham Primary School

Spain

I catch a plane to go to Spain
It starts to rain when my sister's a pain
In Spain we take a trip down memory lane
We have fun on beaches, everyone has peaches
If we have ice cream we eat them in a team.

Heather comes over and says, 'Yum-yum,
What's going on in your tum?'
We have fun with everyone now come on down to Spain
And you may be able to catch a plane
Monarch is the best, you will get more rest.

Chloe Jessop (9)
Ightham Primary School

Winter Poem

White snow
Let's go

Very cold
Been told

Hats scarves
Many laughs

Snowball fight
Mummy's right

Someone hurt
Be alert

Everyone yappy
Very happy.

Courtney Whitehead (8)
Ightham Primary School

I Like Dancing

I like dancing it is fun
I like dancing join the fun
I like dancing can't you see?
I like dancing come with me
I like dancing ballet and tap
I like dancing with hands that clap
I like dancing swirling around
I like dancing hearing the sound
I like dancing, the clothes I wear
I like dancing in a pair
I like dancing, I really do
I like dancing
Shall I show you?

Gabrielle Harvey (7)
Ightham Primary School

Summertime

Gentle breeze
Flow through trees
Butterflies and buzzing bees
Flowers grow
Start out low
End up so they start to show
Children will grin
The summer begins
And the sun shines endlessly

Happy days
Adults lay
And children run around and play
Sunshine fun
Summer's begun
Eating creamy ice creams yum!
The blue, blue sky, the sunny weather
The air is smooth just like a feather
But oh so soon,
With the autumn moon
A telling chill is in the air
Marks the end of the summer fair.

Imogen Harvey (9)
Ightham Primary School

What Am I?

I am sparkly and small
I live up in space
I won't hear if you start to call
I'm in a dark place
I am always with the moon
You wish upon me
If you let go of your balloon
It will soon be with me!

Francesca Bennell (9)
Ightham Primary School

Summertime

Sun comes to say hello
Bees buzzing to and fro

Summer breeze
Wind blowing through the trees

Flowers growing
Rivers flowing

Boys swimming
Girls singing

Licking ice creams
Playing in streams

Butterflies fly
Up high in the sky

Now the sun is no longer high
To summer, it's time to say goodbye.

Callie Birch (9)
Ightham Primary School

Why?

Mum: 'Get you're shoes on.'
Son: 'Why?'
Mum: 'Because we need some food.'
Son: 'Why?'
Mum: 'We're hungry.'
Son: 'Why?'
Mum: 'Are you hungry?'
Son: 'Yeah, but why?'
Mum: 'I'll get you some sweets.' (Bribe voice.)
Son: 'Yaba-daba-doo, yeah hoo!'

Antony Clement (8)
Newington Junior Foundation School

An Alphabet Poem

A is for Albert who breaks all of his toys
B is for Betty who runs after boys
C is for Clara with the red sniffy nose
D is for Derek who has got smelly toes
E is for Edward, he never washes his face
F is for Fred who looks a disgrace
G is for George who likes food
H is for Heather who is in a bad mood
I is for Ian who is very bright
J is for James who is not a very nice sight
K is for Kris who works very hard
L is for Lara who is behind bars
M is for Megan who is a pain
N is for Nelly who has a friend called Kane
O is for Oliver who likes phones
P is for Paige who likes all tones
Q is for Quentin who plays all day
R is for Roy, lives down a different lane
S is for Scott who rides a bike
T is for Tom who has a fight
U is for Ursula who likes ants
V is for Vince who has ants in his pants
W is for Wayne who is nice
X is for Xanthan who has lots of mice
Y is for Yar Yar who likes to run
Z is for Zubes who likes lots of fun.

Paige Wilson (9)
Newington Junior Foundation School

Why?

'Come on, time to go to school.'
'Why?'
'Because you have to.'
'Why?'
'I don't know, just come on.'
'Why?'
'We've only got five minutes.'
'Why?'
'Because that's the time.'
'Why?'
'I don't know.'
'Why?'
'Because I didn't learn that much.'
'Why?'
'Just come on.'
'Why?'
'I'll get you some sweets.'
'Where?'
'At the shop.'
'Why?'
'Because that's how we get sweets.'
'Why?'
'Because that's how it was made.'
'Why?'
'I don't know.'
'Why?'
'Just come on.'
'Why?'
'Come on!'
'OK, OK, OK.'

Allan Ladd (8)
Newington Junior Foundation School

Why Me?

Why me?
Why me?
Why do you break my stuff?
Why do you take my lunch money?
Why me?
Why me?
Why do you hit me?
Why do you punch me?
Why me?
Why me?
Is it because I'm small and you are big?
Please stop!

Abbigail East
Newington Junior Foundation School

Conversation Poem

'Who turned on the sound?'
'Not me.'
'Who played around with the phone?'
'Not me.'
'Who wrote on the wall?'
'Not me.'
'Who played on the computer?'
'Not me.'
'Whose footprints are they?'
'Mine!'

Jasmine Queen (9)
Newington Junior Foundation School

Cars

Cars, cars
Cars are cool like a Porsche
Cars are cool like a Ferrari
And
A
Lotus Elise
RUF
Lexus
BMW
Nissan
Opel
The one for
Me
Is
A
Porsche
And it's
Only for
Me
Cars, cars.

Stuart Sheppard
Newington Junior Foundation School

New Year Resolutions

This year I will try to help my grandad in his wheelchair
This year I will help all of my family
This year I will listen to my teacher everyday
This year I will learn all of my times tables
This year I will do my best at all times at school.

Amy Cook (9)
Newington Junior Foundation School

The Witches' Sea

(Inspired by Macbeth)

'Double, double toil and trouble
Fire burn and cauldron bubble'
To make this spell
A spider's leg
And a chopped up peg
A bit of the sun
Ahhahoo cross bun
A little boy's hat
And a vampire's bat
A big, bad dragon's claw
And a baby lion's roar
A little child's liver
And a long snake's slither
A baby's heart
And a nice jam tart
A unicorn's horn
And a rose thorn
A shark's fin
And a little wing
A little mermaid's tail
And a big hole
'Double, double toil and trouble
Fire burn and cauldron bubble'.

Kiah Harding
Newington Junior Foundation School

Bug Chant

Red bugs, bed bugs, crawling up your head bugs
Pink bugs, sink bugs, crawling up your leg bugs
Green bugs, mean bugs, seen bugs, cream bugs
Small bugs, tall bugs, cool bugs
Blink bugs, link bugs.

Marissa Clay (9)
Newington Junior Foundation School

My List Poem

I like to pick my small rose
I like to play football
I like to play with my remote control car
I like my shiny blue bedroom
I like my total 90 football trainers
I like milkshakey modulen?
I like yummy hot dogs
I like jumping on my soft bed
I like my new football kit
I like my small PS2
I like pancakes
I like *enormous* school
I like fantastic art
I like intelligent maths
I like my best friend
I like my new football
I like my old shirt
I like lunchtime
I like me!

Jack Breach (8)
Newington Junior Foundation School

I Get Angry When . . .

Pinar talks to me when I am doing my work
Brother and sister mess up my room
My mum and dad are sad
My sister and brother copy what I say
I get my homework.

Sinead Parker (8)
Newington Junior Foundation School

List Poem For Shoes

Silver shoes
Red shoes
Violet velvet shoes
Gold shoes
Fluffy shoes
Very high-heeled shoes
Flat shoes
Wedge shoes
Lots of strap shoes
Buckled shoes
Laced shoes
For school shoes
Patent shoes
Party shoes
Going bowling shoes
Which ones to choose?

Emma Wicks (9)
Newington Junior Foundation School

A Bullying Poem

B is for bully, you're not nice
U is for unhappiness, when the bully strikes
L is for lad, the person you hurt
L is for the little sobs you heard
Y is for you having a fight!
I is for 'itting someone
N is for a nightmare about you, bully
G is for glad, when you're suspended from school

I is for 'itting someone, bad
S is for sorry, you don't care

B is for bad dreams about you, in the night
A is for apple, the one you stole
D is for dork, you are one.

Daniel Powell (8)
Newington Junior Foundation School

Conversation Poem

'We're going to the shop.'
'Why?'
'To get some sugar because someone's coming round.'
'Who?'
'Grandad.'
'When?'
'In five minutes.'
'What?'
'In five minutes.'
'Where?'
'At our house.'
'Then why are we at the shop?'
'Because we are.'
'But how's he going to get in?'
'It's alright we're going home now.'

Jamie Goldfinch (8)
Newington Junior Foundation School

Dancin' Homer

Dancin' Homer dancin' with beat
Singing to Charlotte Church
While moving his feet.
Bart comes in and says,
'I like your beat
It's looking so totally neat.'

Burns comes in with his team
He turns off the music
Then Homer screams,
'You're not really trying your best
You're looking like a crazy pest.'

How about turning the music to rap
Like Dizzee Rascal or something like that
Then you dance and start to clap
That's it just like *that!*

Luke Menzies (10)
Newington Junior Foundation School

List Poem

Cakes can be brown
They can be yellow
They can be black
They can be orange
They can be red
They can be lots of colours
They can be yummy
They can be chocolatey
They can be plain
They can be orangey
They can be messy
They can be any taste
They can be square
They can be round
They can be triangular
They can be any shape
They can be frozen
They can be baked
They can be eaten raw
They can be coloured
They can be tasted
And leave the best to me!

Jack Dexter (8)
Newington Junior Foundation School

My Friends

Sameena is so very funny,
Sameena makes me laugh.

Chelsea is the smelly one,
She never takes a bath.

Kerry is so very weird,
Kerry is funny too.

Samantha is the gobby one,
I hope she catches the flu.

Katie is so very shy,
And mad about dolphins.

Masuma is the cheeky one,
She always wears a grin.

Rhiannon is the crazy one,
She is always having fun.

Finally . . .

Joe is the heavy one,
He weighs at least one ton.

Daisy Richford (10)
Newington Junior Foundation School

I Wish I Could Fly

I wish I could fly high up in the sky
So the angels will sing me to sleep
I say, 'Goodbye,' and down I fly back
So my mother don't weep.

Atlanta Amato (9)
Newington Junior Foundation School

My Friends

My friends are so special to me
They'll never leave me, you'll see

My friend Daisy
Is kind but crazy
My friend Connie
Is active, not lazy
My friend Charmaine
Is never a pain
My friend Leah
Why don't you meet her?
My friend Katie
Is my matey
My friend Meena
You'll want to see her
If I was you I would always cherish my friends
'Cause you might not know them forever.

Rhiannon Rose (11)
Newington Junior Foundation School

Football

I like to play football
It is a fun sport
I think it's better than playing on a tennis court
I support Chelsea Football Club
I play for my school team
I've once been a sub
Football is the best

I play football every day
I don't get bored, it is great
It is great, anyone would say
It is brilliant
It's the one that rocks
I would never say it's the sport I hate
Football is the best.

Ryan Maudlin (11)
Newington Junior Foundation School

If I Was An Animal

If I was an animal, I would be
A dog, I would be the best
I'd bark at the postman
Better than all the rest

If I was an animal, I would be
A roaring lion, that's what I'd be
King of the jungle
Everyone would be scared of me

If I was an animal, I would be
A dolphin, I would be so bright
I'd play in the water all day
And even in the night

If I was an animal, I would be
An eagle, gliding through the sky
Watching over everyone
I would always fly high

If I was an animal, I would be
Myself, that's what I'd be
I know now what animals I would be
But most important, what I should be is me.

Ryan Rodway (11)
Newington Junior Foundation School

My Friend

Your kindness and your love for people everyone can see,
But the thing I like, is the way you stand by me.
You are very nice and you always care,
On Earth people like you are very rare.

You fulfil my dreams as if they're your own,
If you are far away, I am still not alone.
Because you are there,
And you always care.

Masuma Aktar (11)
Newington Junior Foundation School

My Friends

My friend Daisy is my friend
Even though she drives me round the bend

My friend Katie means a lot
Even though she can loose the plot

My friend Chelsea loves Avril Lavigne
Even though she can be mean

My friend Rhiannon is a good friend
Sometimes she needs to stop driving round the bend

My friend Connie is my forever friend
She is my very best friend

My friend Ryan K makes me smile
When he sees me for a while

My friend Tom makes me laugh
When he gives me a certain look

My friend Sameena is my good friend
Who is always there for me

So there we are you've heard
My fab friends at Newington Junior School.

Charmaine Wheeler (11)
Newington Junior Foundation School

The Roller Coaster Ride

When I sat on the roller coaster
I felt smooth and calm
When the roller coaster moved
The bar was in my palm, when the roller coaster got really high
I saw a parakeet, when the roller coaster slowed
The ride was not so sweet, when the roller coaster went downhill
I would feel the air, when the roller coaster got to the bottom . . .

Jacob Burton (11)
Newington Junior Foundation School

My Favourite Things

I have a cat
He caught a rat
I have a dog
We could see in the fog

I like football
Looked up to by all
I like food
But I get into a mood

I have friends
They drive me round the bends
I love my family
And they bought me a butler called Ramley

I like school
There is a big hall
I like to play
It makes time fly away.

Thomas Newing (11)
Newington Junior Foundation School

Love Hearts

Love hearts we all have in the body
Love hearts we have for everyone
Love hearts we have between you and me
Love hearts we have under the tree

Love I have for my boyfriend
Love is there and always will be
Love is here, there and everywhere
Love is true and sticky like glue

My heart is there, it is my best friend
My heart is alive along with me
My heart is there, if that packs up I'm dead.

Leanne Handy (11)
Newington Junior Foundation School

My Special World

The best way to get there for me
Is my white stretch limo
For you it's best to grow angel wings
Soft as a fluffy white pillow

When you enter my world
Full of imagination
Dreams, hopes and wishes
Colour and creation

Fairy and angel
Magic dust flowing round
The graceful birds
Making a high pitched sound

Diamonds and gold
Shiny jewels
Stay calm and relax
Bubbly bathing pool

It's time to leave
You now have to fly away
Be careful
And maybe I'll see you again someday.

Katie Martin (10)
Newington Junior Foundation School

My Friend

One day I felt alone
My friend was talking to me on the phone
It's very nice that they were talking to me
It makes me feel nice that I am a part to
You are always there for me
When I need you to be
You are my best friend
My best friend ever.

Ruchira Sachdeva (11)
Newington Junior Foundation School

Friends (They Are Now Mad At Me)

Chelsea is the strangest one always upside down
But normally just hanging around

Daisy she has to come next
That's because she is one of the best

Charmaine come on, now she is mad
And often she is really bad

Leah, well she's off the wall
And she'll always make me look the fool

Katie she pretends to be shy
But no she's not, oh my, oh my

Musuma, she is great at art
But the problem is she loves Mozart

Sarah B is mad, the most
She always seems to be a boost

Sameena is the wacky one
And we always catch her sucking her thumb

Jacob - he makes us run
He is the nuttiest one

And then there is marvellous me
Always acting perfectly.

Kerry Little (10)
Newington Junior Foundation School

Bug Chant

Red bugs, dead bugs find them in your head bugs
Night bugs, height bugs find them in your delight bugs
Pink bugs, stink bugs find them in your link bugs
Man bugs, tan bugs find them in your saucepan bugs
Brain bugs, Spain bugs find them in your drain bugs
Sport bugs, short bugs find them in your airport bugs.

Jamie Galloway (9)
Newington Junior Foundation School

The Enchanted Forest

I'll run into the enchanted forest
Where I'll find a unicorn
I'll run into the enchanted forest
Where I'll find a unicorn and a witch
I'll run into the enchanted forest
Where I'll find a unicorn, a witch and Sagittarius
I wish I could run, just run anywhere
I'll run away to another country into a wood
Across the river and with me I'll have my unicorn, witch and Sagittarius

After a couple of years I'll come back to the wood
Across the river with 4 unicorns, 8 witches and 1 Sagittarius
I'll tell this story when I'm old and grey
Remembering it day after day after day.

Connie Baker (11)
Newington Junior Foundation School

Feelings

Feelings are not a toy
A girl has them and so does a boy

Feelings are all around
In the sky and on the ground

Feelings can be kind, feelings can be gentle
They can sometimes be very mental

Feelings are not a toy,
A girl has them and so does a boy.

James Adshead (11)
Newington Junior Foundation School

The Final Breath Of Life

The first day I was put on Earth
That was the day of my birth
But little did I know what was coming
That the cry of death tune was humming

Soon the final day will fall
Then the angels of death will call
That will be the day of our death
The day I'll breathe my last breath

But here I am alive
Therefore I have survived
But if the angels call
My final day will fall

So while you are living your life
Like the shining glimmer of a knife
I suggest you cherish every day
Because if you don't I know it pays.

Alan Clarke (10)
Newington Junior Foundation School

My Best Friend

I have a best friend
I hope our friendship won't ever end
I love her loads as you can see
She means everything to me
I need her more than anything
Just to hear her voice that sings
I need to see her every day
We like each other in every way
Soon we will be moving on
But our friendship won't be gone
She really is my best friend
I need her till the very end.

Sarah Bartlam (11)
Newington Junior Foundation School

The Witches' Spell

(Inspired by Macbeth)

Double, double, toil and trouble
Fire burn and cauldron bubble
A dragon's claw
And a lion's roar
A unicorn horn
And a spiky thorn
Viper's blood
And a pile of mud
A baby's bed
And a dragon's head
A spider's web
And a man's peg
A bird's wing
And a bumblebee's sting
Robert's arm
Hay from a barn
Mermaid's tail
And a big whale
A child's liver
And a snakes slither
A baby's heart
And a dragon's fart
Shark's fin
And birds wing
Shark's tooth
And a horses' hoof
Scorpion's pincer
And Mrs Wincer
A black bat
And a black cat
Double, double toil and trouble
Fire burn and cauldron bubble.

Dominic Crawford (9)
Newington Junior Foundation School

My Inner Sun

Each day you
Grow closer to death
Nearer and nearer with winter's cold breath
My sun goes away so I can't see
The angel of death is calling to me
For all that is good I really do hope
No one will strop but that's why I mope
Everyone screams, everyone shouts, if you ask me
There's no love about
The goodness keeps everything going
Like your heart keeps blood flowing
Sometimes I see love in someone's eye
It makes people, happy even cry.

Some day my sun
Will come out
Soon there'll be
Love about.

But in our time of darkness I know what to say
Love each other and it's a small price to pay.

Jack Robson (11)
Newington Junior Foundation School

A World Of Fairies

Playing games in the sky
Swiftly, softly they flutter by
Splashing in the river drowning their sin
Swimming, singing and dancing
The angels sometimes go and play
They chat and talk all day!
When at night the darkness creeps
Over the world, they go to sleep.

Leah Breach (11)
Newington Junior Foundation School

Fright

The clock struck midnight
And the thunder whipped the windows
All the little children stood in small rows

The painful scream got louder
It gave all the children a fright
The walk of a small shadow
Flickered past the light

The creaky door opened
With no one standing there
The creak of the door
Was followed by a stare

Bloodthirsty eyes
Looked at my face
But when I looked back
They were in a different place

I get out of my chair
And walk to the door
When I turn back round
There's something on the floor

I scream, a loud scream
But no one can hear me
So I scurry up the stairs
And look around clearly

I get into bed
And close my eyes
Hoping that tomorrow
Everything dies.

Chelsea Shambrook (11)
Newington Junior Foundation School

The Thing

Blowing wind all in and out
Its crazy roar like a wrestler's shout
It twists and turns
Its cold then burns
It will push you away
It will mould you like clay
Take your last breath
This may be your death
Curl up in a ball
For it's so strong it will stretch you tall
For this is the thing
You call him king
Or he'll make you go ping.

Sara Terry (11)
Newington Junior Foundation School

An Orange That's Green

There was an orange who was green
He loved the grass, because he couldn't be seen
There was an apple who was blue
He did something stupid in whatever he would do
There was a pear who was pink
The most thing he hated was ink
There was a banana who was brown
He would never frown
That is my poem
I hope you've enjoyed it
Come and see me sometime
Or you can publish it!

Sameena Williamson (10)
Newington Junior Foundation School

An Alphabet Poem

A is for Albert who breaks all his toys
B is for Betty who runs after boys
C is for Clara with the red sniffy nose
D is for Derek who's got smelly toes
E is for Edward, he never washes his face
F is for Fred who looks a disgrace
G is for Gina who is really big
H is for Harry who would like to wear a wig
I is for Irene who looks like me
J is for Jessica who stole the class key!
K is for Katie who acts like a mum
L is for Laura who has a big bum
M is for Maria who broke her back
N is for Norman whose bones go crack!
O is for Oliver who likes cod
P is for Paige who thinks she's a god
Q is for Quentin with fat eyes
R is for Richard who always lies
S is for Samuel who likes lime
T is for Tina who always mimes
U is for Una who likes lollies
V is for Veronica who has lots of dollies
W is for William who wants a beard
X is for Xana who looks weird
Y is for Yvonne who likes gold
Z is for Zara who has a great cold.

Lauren Ellender (9)
Newington Junior Foundation School

My Big Sister

She's a hero
Not a zero
We've been through a lot
Through cold and hot
She's there if I need her
She's there if I don't

She's my world, my life
My home, my shelter
We argue and bicker
Just like a twister
But she'll always be
My big sister!

Chloe Chance (11)
Newington Junior Foundation School

Pets

My pet is a dog
He eats frogs
My pet is a cat
He is so fat
My pet is a duck
He gives me luck
My pet is a cow
He doesn't go moo he goes now!
My pet is the best
He's never a mess.

Pinar Karaoglan (9)
Newington Junior Foundation School

Down Behind The Dustbin

(Based on 'Down Behind the Dustbin' by Michael Rosen)

Down behind the dustbin
I met a dog called Pete,
'Leave me alone,' he says
'I need to wash my feet.'

Down behind the dustbin
I met a dog called Lou,
'Leave me alone,' she says
'I've got the flu.'

Down behind the dustbin
I met a dog called Rod,
'Leave me alone,' he says
'I need to eat my cod.'

Down behind the dustbin
I met a dog called Frank,
'Leave me alone,' he says
'I'm going to play a prank.'

Down behind the dustbin
I met a dog called Freddy,
'Leave me alone,' he says
'I need to hug my teddy.'

Annie England (8)
Newington Junior Foundation School

The Cat

The little cat that's not a bat
And doesn't know where to go
He looks at his tail and he finds a whale
And then his tail goes stale
The little cat that's not a bat
Finds a snail and calls him Gail.

Nikitta Kelly (9)
Newington Junior Foundation School

Down Behind The Dustbin
(Based on 'Down Behind the Dustbin' by Michael Rosen)

Down behind the dustbin
I met a dog called Pete,
'Leave me alone,' he said
'I'm just washing my feet.'

Down behind the dustbin
I met a dog called Frank,
'Do you own this place,' I said
'No, I've got to borrow money from the massive bank.'

Down behind the dustbin
I meet a dog called Jess,
'What are you doing here?' I said
'I'm cleaning up my yucky mess.'

Leon Whittle-Darrock (9)
Newington Junior Foundation School

Down Behind The Dustbin
(Inspired by 'Down Behind the Dustbin' by Michael Rosen)

Down behind the dustbin
I met a dog called Sam
Down behind the dustbin
He gave me too much ham
Down behind the dustbin
I met a dog called Blake
Down behind the dustbin
He dives into the lake
Down behind the dustbin
I met a dog called Dan
Down behind the dustbin
He ran, ran, ran.

Ben England (8)
Newington Junior Foundation School

Bug Chant

Red bugs, dead bugs
Find them on your shed bugs
Green bugs, clean bugs,
Lanky long and bean bugs
Pink bugs, think bugs
Swimming in your sink bugs
Yellow bugs, mellow bugs
Lazy little hello bugs
White bugs, delight bugs
Buzzing round your kite bugs
Black bugs, attack bugs
Climbing up your back bugs
Blue bugs, new bugs
Find them in Dr Who bugs.

Abigail Ingram (8)
Newington Junior Foundation School

Bug Chant

Green bugs, clean bugs
Lanky long and keen bugs

Pink bugs, stink bugs
Swimming in your sink bugs

Yellow bugs, meadow bugs
Lazy little mellow bugs

Black bugs, pack bugs
Find them on your back bugs.

John Buchanan (9)
Newington Junior Foundation School

This Is How I Got Here

Growing inside you
Building my strength
My arms and legs
Are starting to length

My heart and my lungs
Are starting to pump
Soon your belly
Will be one big lump

Ten little fingers
Ten little toes
A beautiful smile
And a cute button nose

A girl or a boy?
I do not know
What is my name?
Billy? Jo?

Now I am too big
I am too big for you
The time has now come
Your pregnancy is through

Just a little further
I'm nearly out
Is this the real world
I've been dreaming about?

Amy James (9)
Newington Junior Foundation School

The Magic Toy Box

(Based on 'Magic Box' by Kit Wright)

In the toy box I would have . . .
Bright red skipping ropes.

In the toy box I would have . . .
Big blue stilts.

In the box I would have . . .
Long brown skis.

In the box I would have . . .
A big brown teddy bear, fluffy and soft.

In the box I would have . . .
My pride and joy.

In the box I would have . . .
Dolls of my mum and dad.

In the box I would have . . .
Pearly-white marbles of dreams.

In the box I would have . . .
The joy of playing with my friends.

In the box I would have . . .
The pride of all my toys.

In the box I would have . . .
The love of all my family.

My box would be made from
The shiniest metal and spots of gold and silver.

I would put the box in a secret land,
In my dreams.

Liam Sturgess (10)
Nonington CE Primary School

In The Playground

In the playground
Where the skipping ropes go *swish, swish.*
In the playground
Where the children say, 'Mrs Thorn, Mrs Thorn.'
In the playground
Where the girls talk, *chatter, chatter.*
In the playground
Where the playhouse doors go *bang, bang.*
In the playground
Where people run, *pound, pound.*
In the playground,
Children play,
Chatter, chatter, swish, swish.
Mrs Thorn, Mrs Thorn, bang, bang, thud, thud,
Swish, swish, scream, scream.
In the playground
Where the parents wait,
Chatter, chatter.
In the playground
At the end of school, all is quiet.

Sarah Rosser (10)
Nonington CE Primary School

Ross

There was a young boy called Ross,
Whose face was terribly cross,
He started to frown,
But his trousers fell down,
So he blushed like pink candyfloss!

Ross Brown (10)
Nonington CE Primary School

Ben's Box

(Based on 'Magic Box' by Kit Wright)

In my toy box I would put . . .
A handful of children.

In my box I would put . . .
A grumpy teacher.

In my box I would put . . .
Three wishes.

My box would be made from
The finest golden threads.

I would put my box
In my dreams,
So no one could find it.

Ben Giles (11)
Nonington CE Primary School

The Playground

The door opens onto the playground
And then you hear the screams of joy.
The lashing of the skipping ropes,
The hip-hop of the hopscotch.
The joy of scoring a goal,
The bouncing of balls,
The ping of the ball when it hits the racket
And the calm of the dinner lady.

Jordan Heslop (11)
Nonington CE Primary School

The Playground

I'm playing in the playground,
Playing in the playground,
All day long,
All day long.

There's whooshing in the playground,
Whooshing in the playground,
All day long,
All day long.

There's screaming in the playground,
Screaming in the playground,
All day long,
All day long.

There's crying in the playground,
Playing in the playground,
All day long,
All day long.

There are bells in the playground,
Bells in the playground,
It's the end of play!

Robbie Stewart (9)
Nonington CE Primary School

A Foggy Day

Looking out of my dusty window,
seeing fog over the meadow.
The ground is covered with layers of mist,
all you can see are the birds in the nest.
The floor is cloud, the air is damp,
but all that cloud is in a cramp.
For in the sky it is all blue
and that's because the day is new.

Matthew Ford (10)
Nonington CE Primary School

In The Playground

In the playground,
In the playground,
The ropes go round and round,
In the playground,
In the playground,
The balls go up and down.

In the playground,
In the playground,
Children run around,
In the playground,
In the playground,
People having fun,
Yeah!

In the playground,
The mighty playground,
Jumping all around,
In the playground,
The mighty playground,
Hopscotch, hopscotch on the go.
Hey!

Alastair Stewart (11)
Nonington CE Primary School

In The Playground

In the playground,
ropes are spinning.
People are jumping up and down,
teachers are frowning.

Balls are flying,
people are crying.
Children shouting,
running, skipping, also talking,
in the exciting playground.

Tom Beer (11)
Nonington CE Primary School

My Classroom

My classroom is quiet,
Only a gentle whisper,
But when the teacher goes out,
Everyone screams and shouts,
'I had cake last night.'
Scream, shout, scream, shout.
'I got in a fight last night.'
Scream, shout, scream, shout.
'My mum's got a new car.'
Scream, shout, scream, shout.
'My nan's moved far.'
It carries on like this for as long as we can,
But our teacher puts up her hand,
She speaks so loudly,
'No more!'
My classroom is quiet.

Sophie Rogers (10)
Nonington CE Primary School

Wishes

I wish as much as I like
And all my wishes would come true.
I wish I could drive a jumbo jet
And go to places that were new.
I wish I could be a kangaroo
And hop all over the outback.
I wish I could have parents
Who were there, the wish came true,
The parents were there!
The parents I wished for were always there.

Luke Smith (10)
Nonington CE Primary School

The Playground

In the playground every day,
The children come out to play,
They run around all the time
And they run into the school when the clock strikes nine.
Then at lunchtime they come out again,
After working hard with their pens,
They eat their lunches while talking to their friends
And later on their playtime ends.

Every day they have lots of fun,
They jump, laugh and also run,
When they're learning they play as well
And they run out when they hear the bell.
If you listen in the playground now,
There are lots of noises like *slap* and *wow*,
Then there's fun at the end of the day
And the children come out and shout, 'Hooray!'

Charlotte Pape (10)
Nonington CE Primary School

Springtime

Winter's wind, so cold and strong,
Will spring ever come along?
The freezing frost, so shiny and icy,
Spring weather would do so nicely,
When it's gotten cold, all hope is gone . . .
Spring finally comes along,
She's back from her holiday and happy as ever,
The cold wind turns to warm, sunny weather,
She sprinkles blossom all over the trees,
No one can see her, not you or me!
Out of the clouds, what can you see?
It's the sun that shines over the sea,
When we get sleepy and need to rest our heads,
Spring blows her kiss and tucks us up in bed!

Natalie Read (11)
Nonington CE Primary School

A Winter Playground

The teachers drinking their tea to warm them up,
Drinking from a warm cup.
Some are eating mince pies,
While they listen to all the lies.

Children throwing snowballs,
While the teacher calls, 'Don't throw snowballs!'
They carry on anyway,
Having fun while they play.

Oops! Someone's just slipped on the ice,
Oh that gave the teacher a fright,
She rushes over to see if they're alright,
While the boys are having a fight.

'Miss, he's just thrown my ball over the fence.'
'Well, he nicked my 50 pence.'
'James first, have your say,
Then I'll put you in with the little ones straight away.'

The white-washing snow lying on the ground,
The wind like a wolf with its hound,
The children going into warm up and play,
It's like that in the playground every day.

Louise Harrison (11)
Nonington CE Primary School

Loneliness

Loneliness smells like gone off milk.
Loneliness sounds silent, like nobody is there.
Loneliness looks like a ghost staring at you.
Loneliness is white, plain.
Loneliness tastes sour.
Loneliness feels like someone is stabbing your heart.
You feel like you're not wanted anywhere.
Loneliness makes you feel like you're nothing!

Sophie Wallis
Normandy Primary School

Happiness Is Like . . .

H aving a newborn baby being alive,
A s happy as a colourful rainbow,
P erfect as a hot sunny day,
P urring like a happy lazy pussycat,
I nside I feel I'll burst with joy,
N ever want to be sad again,
E agles soaring on the breeze,
S lowly falling asleep in my comfy bed,
S omeone giving me a kiss and a hug!

That's what happiness means to me.

Chloe Haynes (10)
Normandy Primary School

Fear . . .

I fear this thing
I fear that one day it will come and destroy me
I never want to get up - I feel safe under my bedcovers
I dread it every day
Every time I look in the mirror I see it behind me
I feel cold, I feel alone
It's like it has cast a winter's spell on me
I feel fear
It never goes away.

Lucie Eyles (11)
Normandy Primary School

France

There once was a boy from France
Who has always been known to dance
He went round the town
And then he fell down
So he's forever been in a trance!

Hannah Beacock-Evans (11)
Normandy Primary School

Sadness

Sadness feels like . . .
You're lonely.
You're going to cry.
You have no friends.
Everyone makes fun of you.
When your friend isn't your friend.
You're not wanted anywhere.
Sadness feels like you're going to be
On your own forever.
Sadness is a big dark cloud
That follows you everywhere
And rains over you.
Sadness sounds like nobody
Is there for you.
Tastes like a dry and bitter lemon.
Smells like a dead flower.
You feel empty inside.
You're not whole, you're empty,
Until someone wants to be your friend.
You have friends.

Charlie Samuelson (11)
Normandy Primary School

Love

Love is as red as a rose
That makes an aroma up your nose.
Love makes your heart beat fast
And love shall always last.

Love makes you feel all jolly
And at Christmas when you kiss under the holly.
It makes you very cheerful
And glad to be alive.

Ellie Kember-Hollands (11)
Normandy Primary School

Holiday

Sun-scorched skin
And hot crisp sand,
Baby-blue sea,
Foreign friends for free,
Posh hotels and pearly shells,
No rain in Spain.

Hoola-hoola girls twirling round.
Feet burning on the ground.
At the airport,
On the plane,
From Spain,
Back to home in Berlin.

Sasha New (10)
Normandy Primary School

Anger!

Anger is red,
It boils up in your body,
It makes you want to hit,
To kick and shout!

It tastes bitter
And smells like fire,
I clench my fists,
Ready to pounce!

Jay Johnson (11)
Normandy Primary School

All Grown-Ups Say . . .

All grown-ups say . . .
'Don't swear
Don't run in the hall
Brush your hair
Don't be late for school
Tuck in your shirt
Stop throwing pencils
Don't get anyone hurt
Who told you to bring in stencils?
Where's that decimal point, Jim?
Stop picking your nose
Stop talking to him
Jim, stop trying to suck up with that red, red rose
What are you doing?
Where are you going?'
Grown-ups, make up your mind
We're only children!

Voke Oyeye (11)
Parkway Primary School

The Cave Monster

Down in the dark, dark cave,
I met a monster called Jim.
He was very scary,
But I became friends with him.

We played all night and day,
We never stopped for dinner.
When we have a race,
He is always the winner.

When he has finished his dinner,
You can always see his jaws
And you wait a few seconds,
Then he burps and roars.

Matthew Knight (11)
Parkway Primary School

Grown-Ups

Grown-ups are such a pain,
They're always saying things like . . .
'Come over here, Tom,
Get rid of that water bomb,
Stop mucking around,
Tuck your shirt in,
What are you doing now?
Don't swear,
Brush your hair,
Don't pick your nose,
Put down that hose,
Less noise,
Get to school,
Don't bring your ball,
Act your age, not your shoe size,'
See now, you might believe me,
So come down and free me,
Please!

Victoria England (10)
Parkway Primary School

Teachers Say Things Like . . .

Teachers say things like . . .
'Take your hands out of your pockets
Sit down
Fold your arms
Stand up properly
Get on with your work
Look at me when I'm talking to you
Don't argue with adults
Stop daydreaming
Stop wandering around the room.'

Derrick Major (11)
Parkway Primary School

The Old And Elderly

The old and elderly always say . . .
'Don't slouch!
Respect your elders
Do you ever stop?
(Do they ever stop?)
Calm down
Sit down
Don't shout
Stop it right this minute
Act your age, not your shoe size
Tidy your room
Don't even think about it
Think about what you're going to say
Before you say it!
Have you done your homework?
You're grounded
You will appreciate it when you're older
(Yeah, ha ha)
What have you done now?
Why are you in trouble?
What are you doing?
Back in my day . . .
Not even one word out of you!'

Annie Jones (11)
Parkway Primary School

My Mum Says Things Like . . .

My mum says things like . . .
'Make your bed
Get dressed quickly
What are you doing up there?
Eat your breakfast
Eat what you are given
Have you done your homework?
Don't eat and play at the same time
Wash up
Don't eat so many snacks before dinner
Tidy your bedroom
I don't want to see you wearing that top now.'
And by the time I've done all her commands . . .
I have to be ready for her next set!

Christine Tang (11)
Parkway Primary School

Mum And Dad

Mum and Dad are a pain
Because they say things like . . .
'Tidy up
Wash the plates
Go and do your homework
Fetch this
What are you doing?
Eat up
Where are you going?
Stop playing
Have you ironed your uniform?
Feed your pet
Make your own mind up.'

Sarah Baker (11)
Parkway Primary School

People At Home Say Things Like . . .

People at home says things like . . .
'Tidy up
Wash the plates
Fetch this
Get me the hammer
What are you doing?
Eat up
Go and do your homework
Stop playing with water bombs
Where are you going?
Have you ironed your uniform?
Make your own mind up!'

Amanda Pappoe (10)
Parkway Primary School

Adults Say Things Like . . .

Adults say things like . . .
'Have you tidied your room?'
'Yes, but where's the broom?'
'I thought you took it in your room?'
'No!'
'Why are you being rude?'
'I'm not!'
'Upstairs in your room, now you have a mood!'
'Why?'
'Because you're being rude and you have a mood.'
'But!'
'Now!'
Wow, I've never seen her like that before.

Laura Keane (11)
Parkway Primary School

Underneath The Staircase

Underneath the staircase
I met a mouse called Del
I didn't like him
Cos he was as bad as Hell

Underneath the staircase
I met a cat called Ted
He was very lazy
Sleeping all day in his bed

Underneath the staircase
I met a horse called Hutty
She was very annoying
Cos she was a bit nutty.

Zahra Sadi (10)
Parkway Primary School

Love

Love is like lots of luck
Especially for you and me
Love is like lots of luck
Because we have the special *key*

Love is like a red rose
Look up you will see . . .
Love is like a red rose
Because we have the special *key*

Love is like blue violets
You and me are to be . . .
Love is like blue violets
Because we have the special *key*.

Georgie Benton (10)
Parkway Primary School

My Dad Says Things Like . . .

My dad says things like . . .
'Be back at 9pm
Be back at 8.30pm if you are on your bike
Eat your food and finish
Get to bed now, Shane
Clear you room before you go outside
Is your room done yet?
Turn your TV off now
Get up now, it's 8 o'clock, are you up yet?
Make sure you do your lunch
Have you done it?
Make sure you have a drink for lunch.'

Shane Murphy (11)
Parkway Primary School

Grown-Ups

Grown-ups are so bossy and say things like . . .
'Don't talk back
Stop shouting
Stop being disgusting
Take your elbows off the table
Can you sit up?
Go to your room
Pull your socks up
Stop that
Can't you do anything good for once in your life?'

William Jenkins (11)
Parkway Primary School

What Adults Say

Adults say things like . . .
'Keep quiet
Don't be rude
Always obey what people say
Say sorry now
Don't do that
Go downstairs
Why are you standing there?
Don't talk when you're eating
Say thank you.'

Tosin Osiewu-Seriki (10)
Parkway Primary School

River

Down the steep mountain a river flows,
A deep cut in the ground where water shows.
I flow through cities where I am wide,
When I am flowing, time I bide.

When I'm four metres wide, I am a river
And when I'm polluted, I get in a dither.
Eventually I get to the sea,
Where great ocean liners go through me.

Dominic Woodcock (11)
Pembury Primary School

What Am I?

I have four paws,
On which I have some claws,
Which help me stand on the floor.

I have some fur
And always want to purr
And I'm smaller than an otter.

I sleep at night,
When there's not much light
And with my own kind I might fight.

What am I?
A: A guinea pig.

Marcus McCloud (11)
Pembury Primary School

A Water Poem

I can give life to a tiny flower
and be an object of immense power.

I can make monumental towers shake
and many innocent lives I can take.

When people pollute me, I feel sad
then my hatred controls me and turns me bad.

I can cause trouble when I am stressed
but I can be gentle when I am at rest.

Christopher Ithier (11)
Pembury Primary School

Water

I can fall from the sky
When I'm up there, it looks like I can fly
I can become a small stream
You don't want to see me when I am extreme

I have so much power
I can even create a flower
I am fun to swim in
I can be fat or thin

One minute you see me, the next you don't
It is always reassuring to know you can float
I can go fast and I can go slow
But sometimes I can be a steady flow.

James Davis (10)
Pembury Primary School

The Hamster

I live behind bars of steel,
I run around in my little exercise wheel.

When I am ill or if I am cold and wet,
My friendly master takes me to the vet.

Hold me right,
Not too loose, not too tight.

I can swing on the cage bars like a clown,
Don't put me near water, I can't swim, I'll drown.

So there you are, I've told you I can be vicious,
But please still love me, I'm not that malicious.

Jack Welch (11)
Pembury Primary School

The Source Of Life

I can beat down on your windows,
I can beat down on your door,
I can tap dance on the pavement
And make puddles on the floor.

I fill up a big bath,
I think it's called the sea
And when I cry on people
They shout rude things at me.

People do not realise
What I really am,
They all take me for granted,
What I make live - man.

I make many things grow,
But I can also cause pain,
I come down unexpectedly,
So watch out for me . . .
I'm rain!

Rachel Drapper (11)
Pembury Primary School

There Was A Monster

There was a monster from Loch Ness,
Who wore not a kilt but a dress,
It flew up in the air,
He thought this was unfair,
For he did not mean to undress.

Bethanie Walker (10)
Pembury Primary School

Guess My Pet!

Through the kitchen, outside the door,
In a hutch raised off the floor
Lives a creature small and fluffy,
Sometimes neat and sometimes scruffy!

She loves to run and play around,
Never making a single sound.
Her favourite food is cucumber,
She has white and grey fleecy fur.

Her eyes are big, as black as coal,
Her claws are sharp, she's not a mole!
Her nose is wet and very twitchy,
Her whiskers can be quite itchy!

She lives in a two storey hutch,
My family love her very much.
She likes to snuggle in my lap,
Like a baby she takes a nap.

She's cheeky with her little toys,
Ringing her bells, what a noise!
Running up and down her ladder,
Food everywhere she will scatter!

She's really special to us all,
The best pet ever, she's so cool.
These are the clues, have you guessed it?
Yes, well done, it's Lucie Rabbit!

Rosie Woodgate (11)
Pembury Primary School

Windy Day - Cinquain

Flailing,
Trees dance around,
Gusts send leaves flying high
Before lifting them to the ground,
To die.

Oliver Collard (11)
Pembury Primary School

Mountain Stream

Starting off as a stream, at the top of a mountain,
Trickling down, across the purple-grey.

Smooth and flat, I start to swim,
Gliding faster and faster, down this great thing.

Now I am no longer trickling along,
As I fall down, *splash!* into the river.

Great waves of joy, as I glimmer and sparkle
And with me, all the shimmering creatures.

People sitting on all of my banks
And watching me while walking over the bridges.

Coming to the end of my journey,
Slipping into the biggest pool ever.

I crash my waves across the rocks, roaring loudly,
Further away I lie still, silently.

Rebecca Brett (11)
Pembury Primary School

An Air Wrecker

An air wrecker,
An off-road trekker.

A savage killer,
A racing thriller.

A useful pet,
A screeching jet.

A catalogue
To make me a
Car!

Molly Clement (11)
Pembury Primary School

My River

My river is long,
My river is wide,
My river is timid,
But doesn't hide.

It flows along, night and day,
It twinkles like the stars that play.

But watch out!
Don't be fooled!
I can swallow you up
In my deep blue pool!

Zoë Powell (11)
Pembury Primary School

Love

Love is multicoloured
It smells like beautiful daffodils
In a flower bed
Love tastes like chocolate melting
In your mouth
It sounds like the calm sea
It feels like a softy bunny rabbit.

Love lives deep down
At the bottom of your heart!

Ann-Marie Philpot (10)
Pembury Primary School

Ocean

A vicious killer, a life bringer,
A leaping runway, a fast swimmer,
A deep dark place, running like it's a race.
Ocean.

Ellen Turner (10)
Pembury Primary School

Book

An interesting world
Adventure hurled

Intelligence giver
A word river

A fun finder
A boredom blinder

Fact filler
Total thriller

A catalogue
To make me
A book.

Rosie Ivory (11)
Pembury Primary School

Playground

Cold breezes blow across the playground,
Sending shivers down everyone's spines.

The swings rock back and forth,
While gales of wind blow north.

Sounds of laughter echo in the hallway,
Making faint noises during the whole day.

Though during the night,
It's silent, not bright.

Zara Akhtar (11)
Pembury Primary School

A Child In The School Playground

What can you see?
I stood in the screeching playground,
Watching the excited children brush viciously past
                              my drenched clothes.
I saw heavy, big blue raindrops fall on my ice-cold head.
The clouds were dark as the night, like soldiers guarding the sky.

What can you hear?
I heard the wind as it made me shiver down my spine.
It brushed past me as it howled like a wolf in the moonlight.
My ears ignored my friends as they spitefully shouted names at me.
The unhelpful ladies on duty had their umbrellas up as all
                              the children huddle in.
Not me!

What can you feel?
I stood like a stone statue getting soaked right through.
For the fifth time this week I felt lonely, like a goldfish in his bowl.
I felt unhappy, no one to share my worries with.
Then the bell went, dripping, I went into class!

Rosie May Bird Smith (10)
Scotts Park Primary School

The Child In The Playground

A child playing on the slide,
A child swinging on a swing,
A child having lunch with his family,
A child who's playing happily on a nice sunny day,
A child hanging on the monkey bars,
A child spinning on the roundabout,
A child goes to his warm and cosy home.

Harrison Coombes (9)
Scotts Park Primary School

A Child In The Playground

What can you see?
Spiteful bullies kicking and punching with an impact of a gun.
Girls laughing happily, also chatting cheerfully.
Boys darting across the playground quicker than a cheetah.
Young girls crying hysterically as they limp slowly into first aid.

What can you hear?
The deafening screaming of injured children.
The pitter-patter of feet sprinting across the playground.
Quiet murmurs of a lonely young child excluded from the fun games.
Screaming and shouting of jolly children.

What can you feel?
The scorching summer sun shining down onto shouting Scotts Park.
A bloody cut on my knee with purple and black painful bruises.
Bone-chilling winds with the clouds blocking the relaxing sun
                                        from view.
Hyperactive children bumping into me as they have fun.

Sam Firminger (10)
Scotts Park Primary School

The Mousca

The mousca is a funny thing,
It moved so quietly when it was young,
It's even frightened of its mum!
So when his mum found him abandoned,
She said, 'Oh Ka!' (Whatever that means).
The villagers soon knew who took their crops!
Every night the mousca ate his veggies,
But one night I went over to his den
And shouted down the hole,
'Grow your own veggies, OK!'
So after that the mousca grew his own veggies,
But stole a few tools.
He grew tomatoes, cucumber and pepper as well,
So after that, all was well for the mousca!

Ellie Davey (8)
Scotts Park Primary School

A Child In The Playground

What can you see?
A little lonely child as quiet as a mouse.
A few big bullies, bullying a small lonely child.
A few groups of children waiting desperately for their turn in the game.
Big groups of children playing long running races and
                          coming back without any breath.

What can you hear?
A few noisy children chatting and screaming like they just saw a ghost.
Lots of children chanting extremely loudly when someone
                          scores an excellent goal.
Some children screaming very loudly when a child crosses
                          the finish line of the race.
Children crying so loudly when they fall over and injure themselves.

What can you feel?
Invisible wind crashing past my pale white face as I start the long race.
A soft spongy yellow ball hit me on the face when I started running.
Dark green leaves brushing past my rough face really gently.
Tickly grass tickling my very sore ankle as I fall over carelessly.

Chloe Leung (9)
Scotts Park Primary School

Summer And Winter

Children running around and screaming everywhere.
On a hot summer's day you can feel the refreshing air.
I can see people screaming and shouting while
They are having fun and they are playing in the sun.

People screaming as they are being chased
And snowballs are whacked into their faces.
Snowballs flying through the air like an aeroplane.

Abigail Huckle (9)
Scotts Park Primary School

Winter And Summer

What can I see?
Children running happily around the playground
In winter, snowballs flying like an eagle
In summer, petals flying around the melted ground
In winter, children are miserable when it snows too hard for playtime

What can I hear?
Children screaming as I walk to the playground
Teachers shouting when children do stuff wrong
The football net jingling when goals are nearly scored
Children miserable when the bell rings

What can I feel?
In summer, hot sunrays burning inside me
In winter, snowmen always smiling
In summer, children playing hopscotch
Children miserable when their fun is over.

Ben Marchant (10)
Scotts Park Primary School

Playtime!

In February I can see the snow falling from the sky,
Snowmen made when it's settled and dry,
Children wearing warm hats and scarves,
If you're not, you're extremely daft.

In February I can hear the children's laughter,
I can hear snowballs hitting people in the face,
Now no one can see the grass,
If you can, you've got great class.

In February I can feel the cold snow melting in my hands
And in this weather you will not need fans,
The wet snow slipping under my feet,
But no birds are going tweet, tweet, tweet.

Quillan Turner (10)
Scotts Park Primary School

Summer In Scotts Park

Children running around and screaming everywhere
The lovely hot summer's day with refreshing air
Some lying in the shade, some playing football
Proud expressions on their faces when scoring a goal!
Some children performing handstands on the ground
No matter where you are, laughter spreads around

Lush grass brushing on my legs as I run
Footballs crashing on my head like bullets from a gun
The sun is raging on my back
Like a lion about to attack
I can feel somebody tagging me as we play
It doesn't matter what we play, we're going to have fun anyway!

I can hear the bell ring, everyone is sad
It is the end of play, no one can be glad
We go in and hear house captains ranting and raving
Saying, 'Stop talking please' and 'You're misbehaving'
This is what it is like in Scotts Park every day
But in the summer, everything goes your way.

Lily Wright (10)
Scotts Park Primary School

The Elmoust

The Elmoust is a shy creature,
He always finds a place to hide
And even though he is big, he always finds fun,
Elmo is a good friend, once you get to know him,
I like Elmo and he likes me!
Fraistomba was a hard place to grow up for Elmo,
But he still turned out fine!
One day me and Elmo were picking flowers
On our way home and saw a rabbit!
So goodbye!

Stephanie Lipscomb (8)
Scotts Park Primary School

A Child In The School Playground

What can you see?
Oi, Jim's the name and you know what I can see,
That new kid what's-his-name, more to the point, that guy's real cool,
He's got the girls and he's got the guys, what more could
he possibly want?
Sure, he's got detention but the teachers think he's real sweet.

What can you hear?
I still can't remember that Jim-idy-bob,
But I can hear him rapping his rhymes and singing his tunes,
What keeps him real cool is that perfect voice of his,
If he gets a sore throat then he'll go from hero to zero.

What can you hear?
I can't remember his real name but I can think of his nickname,
he's the Super Natural Kid,
He's got hair that's really velvety soft, that's what the girls think
anyway,
They say he feels big and he feels hot, that's why he's the
Super Natural Kid,
Now you've heard of Romeo but who's the Juliet?

Luke Smith (10)
Scotts Park Primary School

The Animagus

The Animagus was once betrayed
But now that beast is never to be seen again
And now he lays, he lays, he lays . . .
And now don't get me wrong, you'll never be seen again
Do not go into his lair, please do not, please do not
Or he will steam up, throw up and he will get very hot
And while Sir Codogan sits up and gets an idea
While the Animagus eats a deer
The brave Sir Codogan makes his way to find the ferocious Animagus
And now the Animagus is on his own
Sir Codogan found his lair and saw the ferocious beast
The Animagus gobbled Sir Codogan in one feast.

Charlie Collin (8)
Scotts Park Primary School

Seasons

As the leaves fall in autumn
We watch the beautiful colours, red, yellow and orange,
The children scream and run while playing games.
They fall over the leaves and graze themselves,
Just before the bell, the house captains run to their places.

In summer, the sun gleams through the clouds,
The children play on the field and pick the grass,
All the little daisies are all bright white as the sun shines on them,
The pond has got lots of reeds round it
And the water sails all slimy as they play.

As the winter snowflakes fall, we throw snowballs
Which are as cold as ice.
The pond freezes up and forms a lake of ice
And the trees gleam white.
The snow starts to melt as the sun pushes
Through the cloudy sky.

In spring, the lovely blossom comes out
And the birds show how they can sing.
The flowers are bright and the bees cutely buzz.
The children pick the flowers and make daisy chains.

Cassidy Roofayel (9)
Scotts Park Primary School

Big Foot

Big Foot slides and wears a disguise.
He wears flowers and says he has powers
And when you feed him, he tries to bite you,
So you have to throw him some food.

He was found in the mountains, hiding behind them,
He eats flowers and says they're sour
And spits them out on the circus floor.

Ellee Penfold (8)
Scotts Park Primary School

Playtime Of The Season

As you enter, you see laughing children running mad
All are happy, none are sad
You hear their laughter under the warming sun
They play on the field, they play and have fun
A breeze hits their faces as they play football all day
And that is the greatest of all summer plays

As you enter, you see a thousand golden leaves
Along with a forest of creaking bare trees
You can feel the rain pattering on your back
You can hear the old leaves give a creak and a crack
The black ceiling of clouds holds back the sun's rays
And that is the coldest of all autumn plays

As you enter, you see a crystal-white field of snow
A playtime of wonders you shall always know
Snowballs flying ever so violently
Breaking the dance of snowflakes falling silently
You can feel their fun, it makes you want to sing
Snowy winter plays are ever so happy, until the bell rings

As you enter, you see rows of budding flowers
But these plays either have sun or showers
There are footballs being kicked
And flowers being picked
The trees are heard to give a creak and a sway
And that is a sunny springtime play.

William Pyle (10)
Scotts Park Primary School

A Child In The Playground

What can you see?
Gorgeous, giggling, girly girls gossiping endlessly.
Big bully boys fighting fiercely.
Sweet seven-year-olds skipping safely.
Little, lonely children crying, friendless.

What can you hear?
Soccer-mad, ballistic boys screaming endlessly
As a ball whizzes into the welcoming net.
A sudden scream of lonely laughter in the far distance.
Horrid, hated words, as a spiteful boy shouts.

What can you feel?
Scared, shaking like mad.
Lonely and left out.
Worried, waiting for the bell to ring.
The school's a zoo, not just a school in a massive crowd.

Sophie Drain (10)
Scotts Park Primary School

Darkness

(Inspired by 'Kensuke's Kingdom' by Michael Morpurgo)

I see the blackness of the night around me.
The silver moon reflecting on the big navy ocean.
The twinkling stars above relax me.
The boat is sailing off into the distance.

I feel nervous, sharks may come soon.
I feel so lonely now the boat has gone.
I am struggling to stay awake.
My mind is full of mixed emotions.

I hear the deafening roar of the bold waves around me.
The loud and clear cry of a seagull gliding above.
The soft wind whistling past me.
My slow and shaky breathing, the boat has gone.

Kate Richards (10)
Scotts Park Primary School

A Child In The Playground

What can you see?
Small, happy, smiling children running crazily everywhere.
Screaming, crying, hurtful children lying on hard floor.
Lonely, sad, unhappy children walking across the line.
Cheerful, chattering children bouncing an orange basketball.

What can you hear?
Tall girls and small girls shouting, 'I caught you!'
Tall boys and small boys yelling, 'We won, we won!'
Screaming boys, girls shouting, 'Help! I hurt my knee.'
A kind little boy yelling, 'You're my best friend.'

What can you feel?
Tiny, enormous stones getting stuck to my hard shoe.
The soft, long, green grass.
A warm breeze of wind brushing against my cheeks.
Green leaves falling off big branches
And landing on my shoulder.

Jade Lay (10)
Scotts Park Primary School

I Am Not Alone

(Inspired by 'Kensuke's Kingdom' by Michael Morpurgo)

I can feel my heart racing as I'm walking through the pitch-black forest.
I can feel my dog breathing heavily on my leg.
I can feel eyes watching my every move.
I can feel the warm breeze stroking my face.

I can see the big rocky mountains up in the distance.
I can see the birds flying over my head.
I can see the sun gently glowing as it rises above the horizon.
I can see the mosquitoes buzzing around me.

I can hear my dog, Stella, breathing heavily on my leg.
I can hear my belly rumbling from all the hunger.
I can hear the wind howling softly.
I can hear the monkeys calling loudly to each other.

Paris Young (11)
Scotts Park Primary School

Playtime!

As we run out of the class,
We see lots of children on the grass,
Playing here and darting there,
Once you're playing, you don't care.

In the spring when you're running from a friend,
The heat really drives you round the bend,
You're so hot, you think you'll explode,
You feel like you're carrying a fiery load.

The end of the playtime is drawing near,
Then all of a sudden you hear . . .
The bell rings and you come off the grass,
You slowly tread off back to class.

In the summer, you run and play
And wish you were in the shade all day,
You're so boiling, on a sweltering day,
You actually wish there was no play!

In the winter, snowballs fly like planes in the sky,
You're so cold, you think you're going to die,
Back in class, it's ever so nice,
You're finally away from all that snow and ice.

In the autumn, you are out at play,
After watching the leaves fall all day,
You get clumps of grass and throw them away,
Then on the grass you lazily lay.

You come in at the end of play,
It's finally the end of a tiring day,
You can go home and play,
But *not* the way you played today.

George O'Connor (10)
Scotts Park Primary School

Playtime

What can I see?
In winter, I can see pure white snow glistening on the ground,
I can see children having snowball fights all around.
In spring I can see raindrops falling all around me,
I can see teachers chatting and having a cup of tea,
I can see children disappointed because it's the end of play.

What can I hear?
In summer I can hear children shouting in laughter,
I can hear teachers shouting even harder,
In autumn I can hear children talking to their friends,
Hoping play will never end,
I can hear the bell ringing, saying it's the end of play.

What can I feel?
In winter I can feel a snowball hitting my face,
I can feel an ice block on my leg, stopping its chase,
In spring I can feel green grass on the ground,
I can feel grass being chucked at me from all around,
I can feel the cold handle of the bell as I ring it for the end of play!

Daniel Leadbeater (10)
Scotts Park Primary School

Happiness

Happiness tastes like a warm sunny day,
Lying on the beach eating a nice ice cream,
It feels like the sun beating against your back,
While you lie back and relax.
It sounds like birds singing happy songs,
While waves crash against the sand,
It tastes like a hot turkey dinner,
With lots of things you like,
It's like paradise with beautiful flowers,
With a see-through sea with golden sand,
It smells like the sun and the beautiful
Flowers and the sand.

Abigail Parker (8)
Scotts Park Primary School

Winter

Winter has come again
And the little boys with trains
I see snowmen being built
And being wrapped up in a quilt
I see snow and snowflakes
Fall from the sky to the ground

I feel wet snowballs in my face
Cold snow soaking my gloves made of lace
The carrot on the snowman's nose
And the snowflake falling on the rose

I hear the snow crunching underneath my feet
And the robins sing *tweet, tweet*
Snow falling from the trees
And it knocks off the rest of the leaves . . .

Ding, dong, ding, dong, ding, dong
The bell has rung.

Joanna Hill (10)
Scotts Park Primary School

A Happy Feeling

When I'm happy I feel like part of a colourful rainbow
When I'm happy I fly in the air
When I'm happy I sail on the seas
When I'm happy I play on the beach
When I'm happy I feel like a bird
When I'm happy I'm in a nice place
When I'm happy I'm lying down
When I'm happy I calm down
When I'm happy I see all things nice
When I'm happy I feel anything
When I'm happy I close my eyes
When I'm happy I fall asleep
When I'm happy I solve bad problems.

Simon Stirling (9)
Scotts Park Primary School

Anger

Anger smells like hot spices and boiling water.
Smoke wafting everywhere.
Heat boiling, burning my tongue.
Water boiled, burning my mouth.
Heat and sweat trickling into my mouth
And onto my tongue, the salty taste was horrid.
Volcanoes erupting nine thousand times.
Drums banging hard.
Nuclear bombs exploding everywhere.
Buses and cars fuming.
Cars hooting every two seconds.
Cars and buses blowing up.
Steam erupting everywhere.
Red-faced people everywhere.
Children throwing stones and rocks.
Kicking a ball through a window.
When my dad's watching TV on Sky Sports News.
When I miss my shot at football against my brother.
When I can't finish watching my TV programme.

Andrew Jones (9)
Scotts Park Primary School

Lizake

Lizake is a cross between a snake and a lizard,
He loves to spin, flip and skid.
I love him because he is helpful,
He's a cleaner when he slides.
It's annoying when he bites,
He lives in a drawer.

Georgia Goodwin (8)
Scotts Park Primary School

Anger

Anger sounds like
Stomping and shouting
And a deafening noise
Banging on the walls with a hammer
Crying with all your might

Anger looks like
Greed and envy
The fury of a red-faced person
And hordes of people
Crowding round

Anger reminds me of
Hatred and
Red bubbling
Jealousy

Anger tastes like
Hot peppers and
Fire with red flames
Up and up
You can taste the salt
From your tears

Anger smells like
Hot simmering food
The smell of something
Garlic

Anger feels like
Heat on your face
With tears steaming
Down your cheek.

Ellice Mansfield (9)
Scotts Park Primary School

Helpless

(Inspired by 'Kensuke's Kingdom' by Michael Morpurgo)

I feel scared
And at the same time, happy
I am scared because I feel very lonely
And I am happy because I am not dead

As I got up from the sand
I stared in amazement
At the monkeys on the trees
And Stella sitting beside me

I walked and I looked around
But I became very quiet when I heard a sound
I could hear hyenas and the gibbons too
I was scared, but I had to find my way through

I continued walking
The wind blowing my hair
I needed a place to stay
Or I would have to sleep on the ground

At last I found a place to stay
It was covered with leaves
It was a dusty old cave.

Jimmy Lagundoye (10)
Scotts Park Primary School

The Panther

The panther can walk slow
He likes to sleep
But if he wants to, he can play with his children
But do not wake him up, because
He will bite you
His wife likes to dance
His children like to play
But best of all, he likes to sleep.

Teniade Obasogie (7)
Scotts Park Primary School

Lurking Shadows

(Inspired by 'Kensuke's Kingdom' by Michael Morpurgo)

I could feel my damp clothes against my skin
And the coldness of my body especially on my chin.
I started feeling a bit upset,
But then came Stella all shivery and wet.

The waves were like one huge gigantic sway,
But the Peggy Sue's engine was just chugging away.
Some of the seagulls started crying for food,
Then I cried out, 'How can you be in the mood?'

Although the sea salt is a very strong taste,
I didn't complain too much because it was a waste.
A taste came to my mouth,
Because it came from the south.

The smell of the sea was too very salty,
In the end I just thought it was cruelty.
Suddenly there was a very odd scent,
I wanted to follow, so I went.

Darkness was all I really could see,
But always knew there was Stella and me.
Except for all the darkness, there was an odd light too,
Probably from the land and even from the Peggy Sue.

The only thing that kept me afloat,
Was my lucky football with its signed coat.
I touched the surface of the rippled sea,
Thought there was a shark, but it was only me.

Richard Stirling (10)
Scotts Park Primary School

The Boat

(Inspired by 'Kensuke's Kingdom' by Michael Morpurgo)

I can see seagulls flying overhead,
I can see the cloudless pure sky,
I can see the clear blue sea underneath the boat,
I can see the dolphins in the distance.

I feel excited and happy,
I feel the cool breeze on my face,
I feel the refreshing sea water against my feet,
I feel the uneven wood on the deck where I sit.

I can hear the peaceful waves,
I can hear the deafening cry of the seagulls,
I can hear the gentle whistle through the sails,
I can hear the boat quietly creaking as the boat rocks.

I can touch the cold metal railings,
I can touch the warm sea water on my fingertips,
I can touch the cool wooden wheel,
I can touch the rough deck of the boat against my hand.

I can taste the sea water as the boat rocks,
I can taste my sandwich as I eat,
I can taste the salty air around me,
I can taste my cool refreshing drink.

I can smell the sea water,
I can smell a wet dog on the deck,
I can smell the wet wood on the deck,
I can smell the baked beans in a pan.

Paige Davies (11)
Scotts Park Primary School

I Am All Alone

(Inspired by 'Kensuke's Kingdom' by Michael Morpurgo)

I can see bright white sand beneath my feet,
I can see coconut trees swaying in the breeze,
I can see monkeys swinging from trees high above me,
I can see the foaming sea, frothing and bubbling.

I can feel loneliness burning inside me,
I can feel longing for my family,
I can feel hunger for food and water,
I can feel tiredness in my limp body.

I can hear the howling of monkeys,
I can hear the growling of Stella Artois,
I can hear my stomach rumbling, desperate for food,
I can hear dry leaves rustling in the breeze.

I can touch warm sand underneath me,
I can touch the sea water that soothes my bites,
I can touch the rough trunks of the coconut trees,
I can touch the jagged rocks on my back while
I lay in my cave, all alone.

Melanie Bevan (11)
Scotts Park Primary School

Sadness

Sadness sounds like someone is crying.
The drop of a baby's tear.

Sadness is the colour blue,
For the tear,
The tear is like a blue sky.
The tear smells like a swimming pool.

It reminds me
Of a little baby dog
And a little baby boy or girl.

The tear tastes like
Dirty water or
Seawater.

It feels like a
Baby crying
In its pram or in its cot.

The tear is like a
Bright blue sky.

Jack Linehan (9)
Scotts Park Primary School

A Child In The Playground

What can you see?
Happy, smiling, screaming children running like hares.
Children playing football, scoring goals with cheeks like roses.
Boys and girls running around, falling over, crying so sad.
Mean, horrible, wicked bullies, kicking hard, punching powerful.

What can you hear?
Shouts of hurt, bleeding children as if they'd been shot.
Screams of children scoring goals, hearts beating non-stop.
Cries of scared children getting told off.
Growls of children, arguing over who gets what.

What can you feel?
Golden leaves falling down onto my shaggy hair.
The pain of my red, raw knee after tripping over my lace.
A hard grab from a friend screaming, 'Tag!' in a great game.
Anger and rage at the end of play bell.

Joshua Silk (10)
Scotts Park Primary School

The Tigeagbear

The tigeagbear lived in an ancient cave
where it liked to sunbathe.
It was the animal of all kind,
but it was difficult to find.
It lived on a diet of mixed nuts,
when people shot him he never had any cuts.
When people see him, he acts like a bugaboo
and they don't have time to say boo to you.
The first one eaten by him
was a little boy called Tim.
When people hear about him,
they always call him a lim.
Someone stabbed him with a flint
and the creature itself became extinct.

Rebecca Travers-Spencer (7)
Scotts Park Primary School

The Darkness Of The Water

(Inspired by 'Kensuke's Kingdom' by Michael Morpurgo)

I taste the salty water while going underneath.
I taste the salty air while bobbing up on top.
I taste the sour fish that pass me by.
I taste the sand from off the beach, maybe it's nearby.

I smell the sourness of the fish.
I smell the salty water as suddenly I go under.
Is this the end? As suddenly I go up I hear
The trees blowing in the breeze.

I see the wave, the wave's coming in like a big mouth
Ready to swallow me into that deep dark hole.
The inky blackness covers the sky with misery.

I touch the cold water surrounding me,
Ready to sweep me along into another land,
This may be the end.

Chloe Brock (11)
Scotts Park Primary School

Engine Tyre

It was a sunny morning
And Engine Tyre was speeding ahead
With something dreadful in his head
He dashed to the park
He drove so fast that he was full of marks
Engine Tyre rolled on a pin
And he got mad and tried to roll to the bin
But a man covered him with wood
Another man noticed him
And picked him up
Fixed his hole
And put him on a pole
Engine Tyre tried to struggle out
But a man picked him up
And put him on a car.

Lawrence Do (8)
Scotts Park Primary School

The Island Of Doom

(Inspired by 'Kensuke's Kingdom' by Michael Morpurgo)

I can see the endless jungle while the morning is rising.
I can see the ocean is as empty as a blank page.
I can see a dark, lonely cave.
I can see red, glowing eyes watching above me.

I can hear the howling of scary monkeys swinging above me.
I can hear the bloodthirsty mosquitoes buzzing around my tired body.
I can hear the wind whistling tome.
I can hear my stomach rumbling for food and water.

I can feel the fresh morning rise upon me in mid-air.
I can feel the warmth of the sun thumping me.
I can feel my burning stings from the mosquito bites.
I can feel the fish and fruit going down my throat.

I can taste the delicious sour fish in my mouth.
I can taste the delicious bananas making my mouth water.
I can taste the spring water striding down my tongue.
I can taste the moist air I breathe in.

Sayed Sadat (11)
Scotts Park Primary School

Peace

(Inspired by 'Kensuke's Kingdom' by Michael Morpurgo)

I can see the vast ocean for miles and miles around,
I can see the Peggy Sue bobbing up and down,
I can see Mum and Dad playing chess below deck,
I can see Stella Artois curled up fast asleep.

I can hear waves rolling around, skimming the sea,
I can hear seagulls calling above Peggy Sue,
I can hear baked bean tins rolling in the cabin,
I can hear chess pieces rattling on their board.

I can touch the waves splashing up against the boat,
I can touch ice-cold railings bordering our vessel,
I can touch Stella's silky soft fur, damp from the sea spray.

I feel that I am free, sailing the lonesome oceans,
I feel that my mind is empty, cleared of modern life,
I feel happy, under no pressure of anything,
I feel tranquil, nothing to disturb me but . . . me.

Sarah Osborn (11)
Scotts Park Primary School

My Day In The Forest

(Inspired by 'Kensuke's Kingdom' by Michael Morpurgo)

I can see monkeys scavenging from tree to tree,
I can see insects scuttling around on the floor,
I can see flies buzzing around the trees,
I can see waves crashing in on the beach.

I can feel vines hanging from the trees, brushing against my face,
I can feel loneliness inside me,
I can feel the heat on my forehead,
I can feel sadness inside me.

I can hear birds singing in the sky,
I can hear waves coming in from the sea,
I can hear the howling of monkeys,
I can hear the burning of my fire.

I can reach out and touch the spider webs,
I can touch the trees that I walk past,
I can touch the heat of my fire,
I can touch the mosquito bites on my legs.

Jacob Muggleton (10)
Scotts Park Primary School

A Child In The School Playground!

What can you see?
I watch lonely, a fight ahead,
Scratching, kicking, pulling the hair on the innocent head.
I sit staring at the child then I hear a cry.
The child's crying, crying, the innocent child's crying is pulling
me closer.

What can you hear?
'I'll get you for this,' he says. I hear, 'I'll get you for this.'
Those powerful words, the powerful words run through my ear.
He hits her and I slowly back away and turn my head.
Then from the same child another cry is heard.

What can you feel?
The thought of a hit runs through my lonely body.
I go to the boy and scream and shout, I scream and shout.
My screaming works, he strides away, a sound,
That's a child in the school playground.

Joanne Maure (10)
Scotts Park Primary School

Wash-Away Island

(Inspired by 'Kensuke's Kingdom' by Michael Morpurgo)

I taste the sourness of the salty air
The taste of my breakfast still lingers in my dry mouth
I scavenge for food scattered on the forest floor, the taste
is rancid and old
As I suck my sore, bitten arms I taste the bitter, sweaty blood

I feel the soothingly cool water lap against my throbbing skin
I can feel the cold, craggy rocks beneath my feet as I climb
the unknown mountains
The eyes tucked in the safety of the forest, watching every movement
The soft warm sand in-between my tired, aching toes

In the cave I smell dank air, musty and ancient
I smell oily fish baking in the scorching sun
The smell of lush, damp mosses and shrubs, fresh from
the morning dew
Coolness tempting me into the jungle's sinister depths

The crackling of my fire is roaring in my sunburnt ears
The wind whistles and howls through the palms, threatening a storm
Trees creak and sway, their boughs about to break
But most of all, the eerie silence that follows, hiding secrets

I feel hunger slowly creeping up inside me
The painful loneliness gradually eating at my heart
How much longer will I survive? The thought is fear itself
I long for the ship that will take me home
But deep inside I know it will never come.

Lidia Guillen (10)
Scotts Park Primary School

A Child In The Playground

What can you see?
Swift, long-legged children sprinting like cheetahs.
Determined football boys running for the ball.
Children running, screaming, hiding from the seeker.
Lonely, sad, glum children sitting on their own.

What can you hear?
Screaming, booing, chanting, shrieking children.
The crying children, upset from bullies.
The upset, hurt, waiting children.
Giggling, laughing, cackling, hurtful bullies.

What can you feel?
Hurt, upset, crying children beneath me.
Blustery wind blowing balls, flying with rage.
Soft flower petals of all colours.
Cold, wet, smooth water visited by the herons.

Lauren Wiseman (10)
Scotts Park Primary School

A Child In The Playground

What can you see?
Laughing, determined children sprinting away.
I watch bullying, scratching, kicking!
I spot a lovely child, wandering around the place!
What else is there to see?

What can you hear?
Spiteful bullies insulting other people.
People listening into other people's conversations.
Children gasping for breath.
What else is there to hear?

What can you feel?
Excitement all through my soul!
Everything's pumped up and ready to go.
Everyone is out of breath.
What else is there to feel?

Amelia Reynolds (10)
Scotts Park Primary School

A Child In The School Playground

What can you see?
Angelic, fast and cunning children dodging people as they run swiftly.
Lonely, tired faces of children, sitting in the corners of the
crowded playground.
Laughing children exchanging toys with pure happy grins on
their muddy faces.
Cheerful boys swaying their arms as they score a magnificent goal
in the world of football.

What can you hear?
Injured children crying and howling while being urged forward by
caring teachers to first aid.
Fierce, growling boys teasing each other with spiteful and
hurtful words.
Mad children gabbling like crazy, with a whole mouthful of tasty
sweets.
Rude, spiteful children telling snobbish tales about other
innocent classmates.

What can you feel?
A hard, fully pumped up ball hitting me by the shin making my
whole body shake.
Getting shoved onto the hard concrete floor by a nervous
football player.
Giggling girls leaning onto me to support their weak bodies from
collapsing with laughter.
The breezy wind swiftly passing a child's red, blushed face of anger.

Rachel Sui Chuen Lee (9)
Scotts Park Primary School

A Child In The Playground

What can you see?
Everything becomes a blur of red and white as all the pupils sprint.
One sporty, long-legged child is playing netball, giving another a hint.
A jostling crowd behind the red line cheering a popular runner on.
Smiles fade quickly and mouths droop as the sparkling sun is gone.

What can you hear?
The cold glistening rain, running down my warm, pointed nose.
Tears welling in my eyes as someone is being brutally bullied
                                                    - it really shows.
My legs wanting to scamper over and join in with the children's play.
There is a swift rush of sympathy towards the child that
                                    accidentally tripped today.

What can you hear?
A bird singing sweetly as a dazzling rainbow forms through
                                                    the fluffy cloud.
Girls just chatting away noisily in the private corner, the
                                    volume is way too loud.
The crashing, heavy footsteps of an older, stronger child,
                                                    the first outside.
A cry of, 'Found you!' from a young one just as they
                                    discover where I hide.

Suyin Haynes (10)
Scotts Park Primary School

Child In The Playground

What can you see?
Swift children carefully marking fast, fit, strong runners.
Lonely children walking around slowly kicking stones gently.
Mysterious children thinking up mighty evil plans to act out.
Caring children helping one another when a child tumbles over.

What can you hear?
Spiteful bullies not touching but using horrible words to upset people.
Loud, sharp, hurtful cries from children who've fallen hard.
Screams of whimpering girls in the freezing rain.
Silly girls crying over silly critical reasons.

What can you feel?
The soft, bright green, long, smooth grass.
The light brown, bumpy bark of the healthy, tall trees.
Grey, spiteful playground with loose stones to trip children up.
Red and black bricks on the walls with gentle generosity.

Sara Bodbin (10)
Scotts Park Primary School

Playtime

I can hear . . .
I can hear children being chased
Running away as they race
Racing away through the playground
Sprinting as fast as they can

I can see . . .
I can see snow all around me
White as a crystal and smoother than a baby
Having snowball fights with lots of laughter
Hiding from the enemy like a seething panther

I can feel . . .
I can feel the long grass on the ground
I can feel the rough goal strings swinging around
Teachers having tea inside the school
Playtime is over and everyone is sad.

Harry Bray (10)
Scotts Park Primary School

Playtime!

I can see . . .
I can see the children shouting as they're being caught,
Children staring as the heron eats the fish.
The football curls in the back of the net,
Children screaming as they just miss the netball net.
They're having fun!

I can hear . . .
I can hear the other children laughing as they have a good play,
They shout happy screams as they run around and play.
I can hear the children being chased, running around as they race,
I can hear the play-pal shout out instructions.
They're having fun!

I can feel . . .
Children can feel the long lush grass as it's put down their backs,
They feel the gravelly playground as they fall down and get a graze.
In winter they can feel the freezing cold snow going
                                    through their gloves,
The children can feel the sting of the freezing cold snowballs
                                        hitting their faces.
They're having fun!

Louie Berry (9)
Scotts Park Primary School

Love Is Blind

Love is where people
Think you're nice
With hugging and kissing
What are you missing?

A thumping heart
Through it is a dart
Love, love, love
A lovely beautiful white dove

It smells like a beautiful
Fresh spring evening
The birds singing
And no one ringing

It tastes like a
Rich chocolate Galaxy
Swirling through your mouth

It reminds you of Valentine's Day
With cards and thoughtful people
And it tells you it's not the look
It's the personality

A rich spring water
And aftershave
Tingling up your spine
And a fresh day.

Josh Butler (9)
Scotts Park Primary School

Humpy

And . . . what is it like?
Oh, it's groovy and movey
It's starry and merry
And bumpy and humpy

And . . . where does it live?
Oh, in ponds and caves
And classrooms and mountains
In houses and waves
And coffins and fountains

And . . . what does it eat?
Oh, TVs and chairs
And lights and trains
Computers and hairs
Tables and planes

And . . . who are its enemies?
Oh, teachers and hobbits
And sandals and dogs
Books and rabbits
Whiteboards and hogs

And . . . what does it wear?
Not a thing
It's bare!

Ellyse Hancock (7)
Scotts Park Primary School

The Child In The Playground

That child over there is cramped in the corner
That child over there looks very sad
That child over there is getting bullied
That child over there is getting hit right now
That child over there looks very cold
That child over there looks like he has no friends
That child over there looks very scruffy
That child over there wants to run away
That child over there is crying with pain
That child over there is wailing with sadness
That child over there is only six years old
That child over there is called Tommy Butler
That child over there is trying to fight back
That child over there looks like a person I know
That child over there doesn't like this school
That child over there has cuts all over him
That child over there only ever cries
That child over there can't wait until he gets home
That child over there needs a friend.

Issy Jackson (8)
Scotts Park Primary School

Deserted

(Inspired by 'Kensuke's Kingdom' by Michael Morpurgo)

I can see the never-ending blue of the enormous ocean in front of me,
The bright full moon that never fails to appear every night,
Mysterious shadows that loom in the deep thick forest.

I can hear the crash of waves as they collapse on the rocks,
The buzzing of the frantic mosquitoes as they try to eat me alive,
The constant raucous howling of the secretive gibbons,
The whistling of the wind as it passes through the trees.

I can feel the cold freshness of the sea as I soothe my bites in it,
The damp beach sand as it clings to my feet,
The jagged rocks on my back as I lie in my cave trying to sleep,
The sweet taste of berries that I scavenged from the forest floor.

I can smell the salty sea which is carried to me by the soft breeze,
The familiar smell of my only companion, my dog,
The dark dampness of my lonely and dreary cave.

Louis Phelps (10)
Scotts Park Primary School

A Child In The Playground

What can you see?
The drifting wind hitting the leaves.
The children running as fast as bees.
The children hide and children cried.
Children walking and children talking.

What can you hear?
The leaves rustling as the wind blows them.
The children stopping as the bell rings.
The trees swaying as the wind blows them.
The children stomping as they run fast.

What can you feel?
The sun hitting my face and cheeks.
The wind blowing my hair.
The ball sways as I kick it.
The leaves hitting my face as the wind blows.

Daniel Butcher (9)
Scotts Park Primary School

The Bumble Botabat

And . . . what is it like?
Oh, it's scavenous and strong
And lippy and lazy
It's dippy and long
And rotten and shaky

And . . . where does it live?
Oh, on laces and in holes
And mazes and flames
In blinds and bowls when playing games

And . . . what does it eat?
Oh, nuts and chips
And squirrels and pears
Bombs and sticks
Leaves and bumblebees

And . . . what does it wear?
Nothing except from its skin!

Shelly Leahy (7)
Scotts Park Primary School

The Bunny Bun

And . . . what does it look like?
Oh, it's hairy and scary
And weighs many tonnes
It's lazy and grazy
Oh, this bunny bun

And . . . where does it live?
Oh, in TVs and holes
And schools and halls
In lunch bags and shoe soles
And pencil cases and stalls

And . . . what does it eat?
Oh, it eats humans and wolves
And kangaroos and ants
And frogs and bears
And trousers and pants

And . . . what does it wear?
It wears anything or it's bare
It doesn't care!

Gabrielle O'Connor (8)
Scotts Park Primary School

The Allsort Monster

And . . . what is it like?
Oh, it's greedy and vicious
And nasty and scary,
It's horrible and ugly
And stripy and spiky.

And . . . where does it live?
Oh, forests and houses
And water and rivers,
Caves and in Heaven
And waterfalls and pots.

And . . . what does it eat?
Oh, zebras and horses and dogs and cats,
Oh, grass and flowers and people and enemies.

And . . . what does it wear?
His skin,
Otherwise he's bare!

Jade O'Connor (8)
Scotts Park Primary School

Washed Up On A Desert Island

(Inspired by 'Kensuke's Kingdom' by Michael Morpurgo)

A splash as the water hits my goose-pimpled legs,
Temporarily paralysed, too shocked to feel the cold,
A boat turns slowly away, abandoning me,
Trying to cry out, but all that comes out is bubbles,
Salt rushes in and oxygen rushes out,
Struggling to breathe.

Gulls cackle overhead, amused by my terrible fate,
Treading water, fighting to stay afloat,
Clinging to my mascot, my symbol of hope,
The sea breeze freezes the bit of me that isn't wet,
Engulfed in murky liquid,
Going under -
Coming up -
Going under -
Coming up -
Going under . . .

I feel the sand beneath my back and the sun beating down,
I lie for a minute, my eyes tight shut,
This feeling could go on forever,
My eyes snap open, alarmed by a howling sound,
I'm on an island, palm trees waving their green fingers at me,
My clothes are dry, my skin blistered,
Slowly the truth sinks in . . .
I am alive.

Mimi Smith (11)
Scotts Park Primary School

Washed Up On A Desert Island

(Inspired by 'Kensuke's Kingdom' by Michael Morpurgo)

I find myself washed up on some unknown island,
My throat is parched and dry and I am ravenous.
I see tall, high trees getting more sparse,
But swaying lazily in the breeze.
I turn back to see the waves,
Crashing violently together against the jagged rocks.
I look up to see the white-hot sun,
Beating its heat on me.
And then I walk towards the trees,
I see twin peaks,
Towering majestically up to the cloudless sky.

I can hear the whoosh of the ocean waves,
And the squawking of the seagull soaring overhead.
A slow rustle of the breeze through the dense jungle,
And the sudden, continual screeching of the gibbons.

I hope I can get rescued by Mum and Dad,
Or anyone really,
But now I must find some food and water,
Or I will die of starvation and dehydration.

I dream of completing our around-the-world sail,
And Mum without her stomach cramps,
Dad getting his job back, and seeing Eddie too,
But now I'm stuck on this island
With an unknown stranger.
I'm scared.

Michael Yip (10)
Scotts Park Primary School

My Sea To Land

(Inspired by 'Kensuke's Kingdom' by Michael Morpurgo)

I can see the gloomy blackness of the rushing sea.
The splashing waves around me as I struggle to stay afloat.
Stella bobbing calmly in the distance.
The odd stars sparkling softly in the sky.

I can feel the cold sea making my legs numb.
The tears stinging my eyes as I struggle not to cry.
The hunger coming as my stomach starts to rumble.
The loneliness of being stranded on a desert island.

I can hear the beat of my own heart in the stillness of the island.
Stella barking happily, coming to greet me.
The creatures of the forest howling and growling.
The trees swaying quietly to the beat of the wind.

I smell the dirty salt from the sea as it drifts in the air.
The heat of the sun on my itchy body.
The humid air all around me.
The sweet scent of newly grown leaves.

I taste the sweet juice of the red bananas, dripping off my mouth.
The sourness of the tinned fish, making my mouth dry.
The refreshing slip of water down my throat.
The milky water from the coconuts.

I touch the dry sand around me.
The rough rocks behind me, cutting my fingers.
The soft hairs on Stella's back for comfort.
My sticky skin as sweat runs down my neck.

Jennifer Igiri (10)
Scotts Park Primary School

Washed Up On A Desert Island

(Inspired by 'Kensuke's Kingdom' by Michael Morpurgo)

What can you see?
I can see juicy, colourful fruits
High up in the lush trees, ripening in the tropical air,
Cracked-open coconuts,
Splattered milk on the white sand.
I can see a small, hidden cave
Surrounded by sand, sitting in the sun.
I turn and look - no one is there,
Nobody has found me, I am all alone.

What can I hear?
I can hear the annoying gibbons
Chatting and howling while they swing in the high trees,
Woodpeckers make me jump
With their tormenting tapping on the hard trees,
The noise of the cracking twigs
Makes my hair stand up on end.

What can you feel?
I can feel the soft sand under my feet,
The warm scented air blowing in my face.
I can feel the hard, painful bites of the dreaded mosquitoes.
I can feel eyes around me,
Someone is watching.

I hope I am rescued safe and sound,
I hope somebody finds me.

Kate Florence Faulkner (11)
Scotts Park Primary School

Washed Up On A Desert Island

(Inspired by 'Kensuke's Kingdom' by Michael Morpurgo)

What can I see?
Pure white, smooth sand glittering in the sunlight,
The immense, rocky hill towering above my head,
The thick, swaying forest, rustling in the breeze,
Raging and frothing waves, crashing against the beach.

What can I hear?
Squawking, screeching parrots chattering away on their perches,
Gibbons howling and hooting, chasing after each other,
The crunching and grinding of sand being crushed beneath my feet,
The snapping of twigs breaking unexpectedly off the trees.

What can I feel?
The blazing sun burning at my shoulders,
The gritty sand stuck between my toes,
The heat and warmth coming from the roaring fire in front of me,
The frozen salty sea water washing over my feet.

What do I hope for?
My mum and dad on their yacht appearing on the horizon,
Fruit and nuts and a meal to fill my stomach,
A stream or river to help my parched mouth,
It's all a dream
And I'm going to wake up soon . . .
I hope.

Andrew Johns (11)
Scotts Park Primary School

Washed Up On A Desert Island

(Inspired by 'Kensuke's Kingdom' by Michael Morpurgo)

I can hear the sound of waves splashing onto the beach,
The smooth warm wind blowing sand over my body,
I can hear the monkeys screeching in the deep dark forest
And the blaring of the seagulls flying over my head.

I can feel the sand running through my toes,
Water trickling up my legs, while the sand sticks all over me.
I can feel the heat of the sun burning my body,
While the mosquitoes bite me to death.

I can see the intelligent monkeys jumping from tree to tree,
The juice from the coconuts dripping like a waterfall,
The sparkle of the sea shining brightly
And the gorgeous trees blowing in the wind.

I can smell the giant, burnt leaves dropping down,
The smell of the strong salty water,
The smell of the scorching sand
And the smell of the lovely coconut milk.

I dream of having my own bed back,
My mum and dad with me to say goodnight,
I dream of my mum's roast dinner
And I dream of how it used to be.

Sophie Rose Boatwright (11)
Scotts Park Primary School

Washed Up On A Desert Island

(Inspired by 'Kensuke's Kingdom' by Michael Morpurgo)

Dear Diary,
I can hear the ocean's waves,
The rustling, crunchy leaves and broken twigs,
Gibbons screaming like a boiling kettle.

Dear Diary,
I can see the juicy, scrumptious fruits,
The phantom eyes staring, wickedly,
A trail of mysterious footprints.

Dear Diary,
I can taste the dark red, sweet bananas,
The slimy, slippery, smelly fish,
The salty, sour sea water.

Dear Diary,
I feel very alone and frightened,
Starving and I think I'm being watched,
My throat is extremely dry and my head is throbbing madly.

Dear Diary,
I dreamt that my mum would come to find me,
I was on the 'Peggy Sue' dreaming
And I wish I never came on this stupid trip.

Emily Wright (11)
Scotts Park Primary School

Washed Up On A Desert Island

(Inspired by 'Kensuke's Kingdom' by Michael Morpurgo)

Big boulders guarding the deep forest,
Peaceful palm trees shadowing the beach,
Miniature mosquitoes circling the fire.

The killer cracking of twigs
And the constant rustling of leaves,
The rioting raucous birds,
Their squawk echoing around the island
And the gibbons screeching high up in the trees.

Exhaustion congesting me entirely,
The funny feeling of being followed,
Really ravenous because of famine,
Hot as the Sahara.

Beautiful bananas, the colour of scarlet,
The great taste of wonderful water,
Row of raw fresh fillets
And the sour salt water that stays in my mouth.

The free fragrance of the sea air,
The smell of smoke circling the fire
And the different types of forest aromas.

What will happen to me?
Will I be struck on this island forever?

Frank Kibble (10)
Scotts Park Primary School

Washed Up On A Desert Island

(Inspired by 'Kensuke's Kingdom' by Michael Morpurgo)

The boat throws me overboard,
The water comes as a shock for me as I splutter and gasp,
I call for my parents, but they can't hear me,
I watch the boat sail away, leaving me in the deep blue sea.

My cries are drowned as well as me,
I feel alone in this freezing ocean,
The stars are my flashlights to Heaven,
As I sleep, I wait for the moment to come.

The smell of fear comes closer as I battle for my life,
Clutching onto my mascot, hoping for the best.
The sound of silence is deafening
And makes me too scared to think,
As I rest in the deep blue sea, my body goes numb.

When I wake up - I'm on an island!
Warm golden sand rustles beneath my feet,
Howling noises echo the surroundings.
The palm trees swoop in the wind,
Showing off their emerald-green leaves.

The island is smallish and the shape of an elongated peanut,
The watch hill shows me this.
I am exhausted and thirsty, everywhere I look for water, I feel watched,
Am I alone on this island?

Alice Smallwood (11)
Scotts Park Primary School

The Cockerwock

And . . . what is it like?
Oh, it's hairy and colourful
And slimy and freaky,
It's fat-eared and horrible
And lazy and beaky.

And . . . where does it live?
Oh, in ponds and deep holes
And water and fires,
In mud and on poles
And caves and pyres.

And . . . what does it eat?
Oh, boiled children and drawers
And diggers and papers,
Then dog bones and mousses
And fountains and scrapers.

And . . . who are its enemies?
Oh, fizzbongs and pelicans
And buzzpangers and bigcags,
Cumbteaches and lemonade
And orangehogs and biggags.

And . . . and . . . what does it wear?
Not a thing,
It's bare!

Abi Morris (7)
Scotts Park Primary School

The Lino

And . . . what is it like?
Oh, it's cruel and horny
And big-headed and moany
It's happy and massive
And stripy and speedy

And . . . where does it live?
Oh, in jungles and rivers
And sandpits and seas
In planets and stars
And fish ponds and leaves

And . . . what does it eat?
Oh, roast lamb and crickets
And fish bones and rocks
Then hobbits and rings
And fish cakes and kings

And . . . who are its enemies?
Oh, horses and deer
And fish and snakes
People and toilets
And posters and rakes

And . . . and . . . what does it wear?
Not a thing
It's bare!

William Goodall (8)
Scotts Park Primary School

The Antelope With 3 Tails

I thought that I was seeing things,
I thought that I'd gone mad,
I thought that it was a mirage
Till I showed my dad.

He had seen it, just as clear,
As clear and as bright as day,
An antelope with 3 long tails,
I just didn't know what to say.

To see an antelope in the street
Was a shock to everyone
And this one had 3 very long tails
And on its back . . . my mum!

She thought that it was lovely,
With its tails so long and hairy,
But all of the babies in their prams
Thought that it was scary.

The antelope danced happily towards the pub for ale
And when I looked, it had 3 pints, one in each tail,
I blinked and blinked again to check that what I saw was true,
But an antelope with 3 tails, I don't think so now, do you?

Ellie Kane (7)
Scotts Park Primary School

The Digleboca-Doto

And . . . what is it like?

Oh, it's dotty and swirly
And smiley and happy
It's colourful and funny
And stupid and silly

And . . . where does it live?

Oh, in cakes and pies
And peach plum hoorah
In black bags and sausages
And apples, happy days

And . . . what does it eat?

Doughnuts and junk food
To make it all funny
Then bins and metal
And clouds and honey

And . . . what does it wear?

Nothing
It's bare!

Lauren Del Guercio (8)
Scotts Park Primary School

A Child In The Playground

I'm sitting on the bench
All by myself
I'm 1.1
But I'm treated like an elf

Nobody likes me
I'm all on my own
All I can hear
Is a happy tone

But I'm not happy
And that's all that counts
'I'm not happy'
I announce

When school's out
I'm glad to go home
I wish this was
A happy poem

I sit on the swings
Thinking of horrible things
My mum says it's OK
Then I met Louie
And said, 'Hooray!'

Hollie Gunns (9)
Scotts Park Primary School

The Playground

In autumn I see leaves fall off the trees
And puddles on the ground,
I hear hail tapping on the windows
And I feel the rain on my head.

In winter I see the frost-covered fields
And snowballs flying like missiles,
I hear the cold wind blowing
And I feel the icy air.

In spring I see the flowers on the bushes
And the leaves back on the trees,
I hear children screaming
And I feel the wind on my face.

In summer I see grass stains and dirt on my shirt
And the sun shining high in the sky,
I hear birds singing
And the bell ringing

And I feel very annoyed!

Patrick Unwin (10)
Scotts Park Primary School

The Child In The Playground

Standing there
Being ignored
No one to play with
Nothing to play
Just standing
Watching
Waiting for someone
To ask me
To play with them
Loving the time
When the bell
Rings in my ears
Lining up
Walking in
Still being ignored
As if I'm not there
But dreading the time
The teacher says
'Go on everyone
Go out to play.'

Jenny Jones (9)
Scotts Park Primary School

Washed Up On A Desert Island

(Inspired by 'Kensuke's Kingdom' by Michael Morpurgo)

What can you see?
The dark and deafening blue ocean,
Creepy, glowing eyes watching me,
Something gleaming, it is a bit like rusted metal,
A half man, half monkey slowly jumping about.

What can you hear?
Gibbons screeching and screaming,
Scraping and scratching noises, giving me a headache,
The evil buzzing of mosquitoes,
Scorching hot flames flickering in the darkness.

What can you taste?
Thin, white and smelly fish,
Red, ripe and sweet bananas,
Cold and dirty saltwater rushing in my mouth.

What do you hope for?
My mother and father will come and collect me,
I will survive - with dirty water
And only a little food.

What do you dream of?
I dream of back home going to school
And my best, best friend, Eddie,
Terrible nightmares too,
Of not surviving on the island.

Jeyda Abakan (11)
Scotts Park Primary School

Washed Up On A Desert Island

(Inspired by 'Kensuke's Kingdom' by Michael Morpurgo)

Dryness, thirstiness through my body,
On my own, feeling lonely with no one to talk to,
Feeling eyes watching me, not letting me out of sight,
Sad but happy, scared but relieved,
For I have survived the ocean,
The deep, dreaded ocean.

Water, water everywhere - but not a drop to drink!
I get my hopes up when I see rocks,
But just ocean water all around,
With soft, dry, dusty, white sand in the shining, scorching sun.

Screeching of the gibbons,
Whooshing of the water,
Suddenly silence . . .
Then scratching and scraping again.

I hope to get off this island,
To get some sleep in a bed or at least a decent place,
To get my lucky football back,
But mostly to see my family and friends
And our favourite boat . . .
'The Peggy Sue'.

Jade-Louise O'Brien (11)
Scotts Park Primary School

Washed Up On A Desert Island

(Inspired by 'Kensuke's Kingdom' by Michael Morpurgo)

I can see the glowing moon glinting over me,
The favoured football bobbing in and out of the waves,
The leaves blasting everywhere on the bland trees,
Different fruits and coconuts in odd places,
Phantom-eyed caves with dry sand inside,
Big bowl of water, palm leaves and translucent fish,
Red bananas and a shadow lurking in the forest.

I hear the strange ghostly sound of singing in the distance,
The terrifying howling of gibbons in the trees,
The frightful crackling of twigs around me,
The faint sound of leaves shivering in the wind,
Mosquitoes whining in my ear every second,
The forest is alive with noise.

I feel overjoyed that I survived the great sea,
Positive that I will be rescued,
Panicky and frightened in the darkness,
Burning heat of the sun's powerful rays early in the morn,
The lovely taste of water when I really need it,
Should I be fearful or overwhelmed?
I'm not alone.

Amy Johnston (11)
Scotts Park Primary School

Washed Up On A Desert Island

(Inspired by 'Kensuke's Kingdom' by Michael Morpurgo)

Deep blue water rushing all around me,
Eddie's white football bobbing up and down,
An island full of green palm trees,
Lovely red bananas lying on the branch.

A ghostly howling sound,
Constant sounds I've never heard before,
Sea splashing against the hard grey rocks,
Rain crashing down onto sea.

Droplets dropping on my head,
I feel as if I am going to die,
Being watched on every side,
Fish nicer than at home.

The noises are making me nervous,
They stop, then start and stop again,
I can taste the sea salt in my mouth,
A fading outline of an ape behind the fire.

I dream I could be off this island,
I dream I could see my parents again,
I dream to be at home with peace at last,
I dream that I could be on the 'Peggy Sue' with Mum and Dad.

Nile Glasgow (10)
Scotts Park Primary School

Washed Up On A Desert Island

(Inspired by 'Kensuke's Kingdom' by Michael Morpurgo)

What can you see?
The lovely white rich sand glowing in the sun,
The 100ft tall trees ascending up into the sky,
An ancient shipwreck washed up in the water,
With a rusted piece of metal beside it.

What can you feel?
The roasting sand tickling my feet,
The awful sun glazing down in my eyes,
The transparent chip of glass burning my hands,
Lots of mosquito bites stinging my arms and legs.

What can you hear?
The terrible gibbons echoing in the forest,
The whine of mosquitoes buzzing in the air,
Branches and twigs blazing in the fire,
A man speaking to me in a foreign language.

What do you dream of?
My mum and dad coming to get me,
Going home and going to my comfortable bed,
Drinking my mum's home-made hot chocolate,
Holding my special football again.

Jay Hancock (10)
Scotts Park Primary School

Washed Up On A Desert Island

(Inspired by 'Kensuke's Kingdom' by Michael Morpurgo)

Sparkly blue sea, glinting back at me,
The monkeys jumping soundly through the trees,
Bright green palm trees with rough trunks,
The seagulls flying over me.

The sand crunching loudly by my feet,
The sound of the waves swishing backwards and forwards,
I can hear the palms' leaves rustling in the wind,
The soft sound of my echoes.

The smell of the salty sea,
The smell of the juicy coconut milk,
The smell of the burning hot sand,
The smell of the rough dried leaves.

The burning hot sand running through my toes,
The water splashing my little legs as hard as it can,
The sand blowing all over my face,
The wonderful cold breeze blowing gently at me.

I really want some delicious food,
I want cold clean water to drink,
A nice cosy bed to sleep in,
But most of all -
My wonderful mum and dad.

Brogan-Alisia Haisell (11)
Scotts Park Primary School

Washed Up On A Desert Island

(Inspired by 'Kensuke's Kingdom' by Michael Morpurgo)

I wake up slowly,
I feel confused and scared, not knowing where I am,
I get to my feet,
I feel the soft sand between my toes,
The warmth of the sun burning on my back,
I'm dying of thirst and hunger,
I feel too sleepy to go on.

I suddenly hear weird noises, grunting and groaning,
Getting louder and louder,
Coming from the deep, dark, dangerous wood.
I suddenly see food, high up in the trees,
The only way to reach them is passing the scary noise.

I fall to the ground,
My body sinking into the warm soft sand,
I can't go on.
As I lie there, I can hear the sound of the cool waves coming in,
The splash as they hit the hard, grey rocks on the shore,
The whooshing, splashing sound echoing in my head,
As I drift off to sleep.

I dream about my mum, my dad
And being rescued by the boat, 'Peggy Sue',
The starve of hunger fading away
And being back in my bed once again.

Rosie Chapman-Anderson (11)
Scotts Park Primary School

Washed Up On A Desert Island

(Inspired by 'Kensuke's Kingdom' by Michael Morpurgo)

The cold open ocean washing around me,
The sea slowly getting shallow,
Warm sand roughly rubbing against my bare back.

The white sand spread out as far as I can see,
A hill further up the island with rocks perched on top,
A wide, fearsome forest covering the island.

Wild gibbons hooting horrendously, never stopping,
Birds screeching, straining their voices,
Dry twigs cracking under my feet.

The wonderful fresh water trickling down my throat,
The slimy, slippery surface of sliced fish,
Sweet red bananas, banging my taste buds.

A small, strange man running at me, shouting angrily,
Wearing worn-out battered breeches,
One large glinting knife glaring back at me,
Stella, the dog, hanging around him.
Why?

Betrayed by my one and only friend,
Being alone is driving me round the bend,
The torture of my cave keeping me awake at night,
'The Peggy Sue' completely out of sight.

Elizabeth Wood (11)
Scotts Park Primary School

Washed Up On A Desert Island

(Inspired by 'Kensuke's Kingdom' by Michael Morpurgo)

Palm trees waving to their left and right,
Monkeys swinging from branch to branch,
Lizards sitting on leaves camouflaged,
I can see green-winged macaw and other birds flitting in
the air like flies.

A sudden screech of a parrot sitting comfortably on a palm tree,
Mosquitoes buzzing around like bees,
Cobra hissing as it slithers away,
The waves rushing to the bright white sand.

I can taste the fish strips I ate five minutes ago,
I can still taste the salt that I had swallowed in the sea,
I feel scared and frightened in the deep, moist forest,
It makes me shiver,
I feel like eating good, delicious food now.
I feel cold, miserable and alone . . .

Ardeshir Boloki (11)
Scotts Park Primary School

A Child In The Playground

What can you see?
Soft, smooth, silky hair blowing in the hushing wind.
Old, tattered, muddy shoes ripped to shreds.
Best buddies blabbering about £20 blue eye mascara.
Rough, scraped football boys fighting for the black and white
checked ball.

What can you hear?
Mouths so wide open you can see the darkness of their red tonsils.
The loud crying of a young person who is bleeding to death.
Loud yelling of someone who has just been caught in the last two
precious minutes.
The loudness of the iron bell giving a loud command to stop.

What can you feel?
The soft, green grass tickling the top of my fingertips.
Whiteness of a little daisy swaying in the cool breeze.
Birds' soft feathers tickling my pale hands.
Prickly brown and orange leaves crackling as you step on them.

Carina Rodger (10)
Scotts Park Primary School

Washed Up On A Desert Island

(Inspired by 'Kensuke's Kingdom' by Michael Morpurgo)

I can see a dirty and damp shipwreck,
Stella looking at me with hunger and thirst,
Birds gliding fiercely out of trees.

I can hear Stella's breath panting madly,
Island creatures yelling at each other,
Stella barking at the creatures that roar.

I can feel eyes watching over me,
The sun sucking the moisture out of me,
The bananas rolling about in my dried-up mouth.

I can taste the warm air flowing into my mouth,
The mouth-watering fish and bananas,
The cold water refilling my mouth.

I can smell the fire burning from the ground,
The sea water going in and out my legs,
The fishes letting off their awful scent.

I dream that a rescue boat will take me away,
To eat whatever I want,
I want to get off this desert island.

Michael Bridger (11)
Scotts Park Primary School

The Things I Love

I love swimming with my mum
I love Towers School
I love having my hair done
I love tasty strawberries
I love cold ice cream
I love scrumptious blueberries
I love looking at rainbows
I love being me
I love smelling red roses
I think these things rule.

Ruby Scobie (10)
Victoria Road Primary School

Loneliness

A is for always being alone
B is for being bored
C is for castle on the hill
D is for despising being alone
E is for everyone else having friends
F is for fiery temper
G is for ghastly moods
H is for handkerchief into which I cry
I is for feeling everyone else is important
J is for jealous
K is for feeling like a knife through the heart
L is for being lonely
M is for moaning
N is for nagging because I am lonely
O is for opportunities missed
P is for people playing alone
Q is for quarrelling with my friends
R is for really crying all night
S is for screaming in my head
T is for having a tantrum
U is for unkind
V is for Valentine's never occurring
W is for whining
X is for Xmas, no presents received
Y is for yo-yo, my feelings go up and down
Z is for zombie when I am feeling lonely.

Lorraine Manyengavana (11)
Victoria Road Primary School

Happy

A is for always being loved
B is for being so caring
C is for cuddling my cats
D is for dancing
E is for seeing an elephant
F is for always having friends
G is for always giggling
H is for going in a hot air balloon
I is for having an ice cream on a hot day
J is for jumping for joy
K is for having a kite
L is for laughing
M is for being like a monkey
N is for naughty things that make me happy
O is for other people that make me smile
P is for going to a party
Q is for meeting the Queen
R is for seeing rainbows
S is for swimming
T is for having a cup of tea
U is for being unhappy
V is for having a vacation
W is for having water
X is for having Xmas
Y is for having a yo-yo
Z is for being in a zany mood.

Georgia Witney (10)
Victoria Road Primary School

Frustration Is Like . . .

Frustration is black and red like a tremendous black hole
Swirled with anger and hatred.
Frustration is like the confusion of an earthquake
and a volcano in one.
Frustration is like wild cannon fire.
Frustration is like a bomb set to blow.
Frustration is like an explosion from a bomb.
Frustration is a wave of fire.
Frustration is a sphere filled with tongues of fire
and pure *frustration*.
Frustration is a wave of flame-like feeling
that will overwhelm you and completely eliminate all other feeling.
And once it starts, hardly anything can redeem you!

Sam Armer (9)
Victoria Road Primary School

Feelings

Hate is . . .
Hate is the colour of the red Devil you have never seen
Hate is the sound of a lion's roar
Hate is the shape of Darth Vader!

Happiness is . . .
Happiness is like the bright yellow sun
Happiness is the sound of a racing car darting past
Happiness is the shape of the sun.

Craig Sherwood (8)
Victoria Road Primary School

Happiness

A is for appreciating life.
B is for being fabulous.
C is for cheering people up.
D is for dancing till you drop.
E is for eager to laugh again and again.
F is for being the first person picked.
G is for getting on with pleasure.
H is for helping for no reason at all.
I is for impressing the hardest of people.
J is for jumping with glee.
K is for keeping everything attached.
L is for laughing till you get hiccups.
M is for monkeying around.
N is for not bothering with bad things.
O is for ordering 'Over-The-Moon' happy thing.
P is for parading the corridors with a smile on my face.
Q is for quiet but feeling great.
R is for rhythm in my bones.
S is for sharing with friends.
T is for tagging along but not left out.
U is for understanding just what's right.
V is for very, very extraordinary.
W is for waving goodbye to your troubles.
X is for xylophones dancing everywhere.
Y is for young and loving it.
Z is for zoos running wild just to see you laugh.

Leanne Crust (10)
Victoria Road Primary School

Love

Love is like two pink diamonds.
Love is like a musical triangle.
Love is like a sphere.

Ryan Dodd (8)
Victoria Road Primary School

Anger

Anger is bad-tempered
Run around like a headless chicken
Strut
Punch
Scream
Swear
Face goes red
Slam doors
Stomp
Wild
Heated
Hot under the collar
Be in a paddy
Flare out
Fiery
Incensed
Ratty
Get stomped up
Wrath out
Vexed
Outraged
Provoked
Dungeon
Put out
Boil
Choked
Ratty
Raving.

Bradley Mackenzie (11)
Victoria Road Primary School

Happy

A is for always having friends
B is for bouncing around
C is for cycling
D is for dancing
E is for exercise
F is for stroking a fox
G is for giggling
H is for hot air balloon
I is for ice cream
J is for joyful
K is for karaoke, singing loud
L is for lambs jumping around
M is for monkeying around
N is for noseying around
O is for objects which make me smile
P is for going to a party
Q is for the Queen
R is for raiding the chocolate box
S is for swimming happily
T is for a trip
U is for unwrapping birthday presents
V is for Valentine cards
W is for feeling on top of the world
X is for Xmas presents
Y is for yellow
Z is for stroking a zebra.

Heleena Castle (11)
Victoria Road Primary School

Love

Love is like a red sun.
I love my football like my bike.
I love cake and I like bacon.

Thomas Myers (8)
Victoria Road Primary School

Anger

Anger is like a red-hot devil breathing fire
Anger is like a sound of an angry snake
Anger is like a bull's horn

Love is like a poppy in the spring
Love is like a beating heart
Love is like red blossom flowing in the air

Hate is like a red burning fire
Hate is like a sound of a horrible dinosaur
Hate is like a shape of a shark's jaw

Happiness is like a yellow smiley face
Happiness is like a crowd of people
Happiness is like a golden face

Sadness is like a red face
Sadness is like the sound of a scream
Sadness is like a bully beating him up.

Nathan Louder (8)
Victoria Road Primary School

Feelings

Hate is . . .
Hate is like the chilli, red with spice,
Hate is like a plane crashing,
Hate is like a sharp spike.

Love is . . .
Love is like the blue waves of the sea,
Crashing on the shore,
Love is the sound of relaxing music,
Love is like a sharp kiss.

Thomas Butler (7)
Victoria Road Primary School

Emotions

Anger is like a big black hole sucking your brain and heart away.
Anger is like a whirling, whooshing tornado blowing you away.
Anger is like lots of black circles in a black hole.

Love is like a white dandelion tickling your flesh.
Love is like the explosion in your heart but it never stops
                                                    beating or cracks.
Love is like the round soft heart in your belly.

Happiness is like a pink rose, prickling you but it never hurts you.
Happiness is the sound of the music of the heart.
Happiness is like the shape of a soft, not prickly rose.

Jack Haylen (8)
Victoria Road Primary School

Love And Happiness

Love is like the white of the dove flying in the air,
Love is like the sound of the sea lapping against the shore,
Love is like the smooth soft circle.

Happiness is like the yellow of a sunflower growing in the
                                                    light of the sun,
Happiness is like the sound of leaves bashing in the breeze,
Happiness is like the crescent of a moon in the night.

Theo Wanstall (8)
Victoria Road Primary School

Good Feelings

Happiness is like the yellow sunshine streaming through my window.
Happiness is like the cheering of the crowd when someone scores.
Happiness is like the blue sky in the air.
Love is like the red rose in your garden.
Love is like the beating heart.
Love is like the tweety bird in the air.

Emily Sharpe (8)
Victoria Road Primary School

Happiness And Love

Happiness is like golden yellow hair.
Happiness is like kids at the beach.
Happiness is like the shape of all my friends.

Love is like the bright pink pig.
Love is like the beating of a heart.
Love is like a petal of a rose blooming in the spring.

Rhianna Le Carpentier-Rogers (8)
Victoria Road Primary School

Colours Of Love

Love is like the red of a love heart
Happiness is like the yellow of the sun
Rain is like the blue of the sky.

Connor Howell (8)
Victoria Road Primary School

My Idea Of Love

Love is like the blue sea with crashing waves.
Love is like listening to good, relaxing music.
Love is like a bent-over rose.

Jake Thirwell (8)
Victoria Road Primary School